LP wake up and have toast every morning, LP use to own 6 fishes,
3 birds one called peter, now own an animal called gelati, likes drawing
and inventing stories, is not professional, enjoys the sun and making some
art stuff, and help grand dad make bottoms
    and talk art stuff and make useless work and feel weird and enjoy
making when it works and provoke and repeat itself for ever and not get
anywhere just repeat again and again and make shows and exhibit thoughts
and idea or inserternties, and be vulnerable and be proud and love and
care and invent and not make sense and not understanding any thing and
not know why making just surviving by not thinking too much by not
carring too much by being light and playfull being with people we love.
By being with people we care for. Miss understanding mis translating miss
comunication as a deffence or not grassping. Making mistakes for ever and
showing what is not shown what is not there what is not try or unexhistant

    laure provost put her left food down
    take 4 steps, push a door, turn to the right the shower hose get in the
shower put soap in her hands put ...

THE
ARTIST
BOOK

LAURE PROUVOST

Book Works

ON THIS
PAGE SHOULD
BE NOTHING

CHAPTER 1

BIOGRAPHY

Early Years

Adolescence

The Artist's Drive

The Artist and Drugs

Being Misunderstood

The Artist's Only Love

The Artist's Special Show

Travels

The Artist's Contemporaries

The Forgotten Artist

Depression

The Artist's Secret

When the artist was fifteen, the artist was bored of school and the people there. It wasn't an ordinary kind of boredom that fifteen-year-olds have; it was a little ugly, like a very dark mole that had started to grow hair. The artist became interested, for sure, in all the things that bored fifteen-year-olds are interested in – *The Clockwork Orange*, The Cure, smoking pot and cigarettes – but also in something less obviously interesting: normality. The artist was obsessed by the constancy of fifteen-year-old rebellion – *The Clockwork Orange*, The Cure, smoking pot and cigarettes – and fell a little in lust with the fifteen-year-olds who liked those things. The artist wanted to move too close to them, and they knew it; the interest in their interests was a little predatory.

It was also around this time that Broadway had another of its inexplicable successes, none of which are inexplicable anymore as it has been proven that they are all a string of revivals, come at the right time for the right baby-boomers. This one was *The Who's Tommy*, which got five stars from all the major papers and broadsheets and which everyone flocked to see. So did the artist, and repeatedly – for in that musical's chilly refrain ('freedom lies in normality') the artist found an answer. The artist loved the theatre, which for a certain type of person, and not the one you might think, is indistinguishable from musicals. The artist loved the artifice, and the controlled expression, and the overt playing of type: the reduction of character to a few communicable traits. The artist went to *Tommy* a few times, and hung outside the stage door afterwards a couple times, to meet the man who played Tommy as he left after the show. The artist was fifteen, and the actor was thirty-three. The artist wanted normality, and aberrance, and was visibly hungry for something not yet known. The actor took the artist to a diner by Times Square. He took the artist's number. They took subways in different directions home.

The artist knew that thirty-three was too old, but also that this thirty-three-year-old was the star of the Broadway production that everyone was flocking to see. The artist thought it was possible to get away with things. The artist's interest in rebellion and its corollaries was also part of a way of thinking that understood the clichés perhaps more than the real. Like seeing the forest and the trees as paper cut-outs: the artist saw how things were seen, and because of this over-developed ability believed in invincibility –

or at least let the word invincible float somewhere in the brain, whether or not the artist believed in it fully. The artist saw the clichés of rebellion, of narcissistic actors, even of a thirty-three-year-old's desire for a fifteen-year-old, which is less of a cliché than a safe bet. I would like to know how much the artist saw reality, or where reality is when you can only see constructions. He called, and they arranged to meet on a Saturday after his matinée.

The artist met him again by the stage door; there are often two in the back of a theatre, and everyone knows which one the stage door is. The performers leave by the main stage door and are not annoyed to see fans waiting – but when celebrities perform they leave by the second stage door, away from the throng of signature-seekers. The Who's *Tommy* left, just this day, by this second stage door, which was the one the artist had guessed he would choose. They had lunch; they went back to his place, an apartment in a high-rise not too far away. He had, unlike most bedrooms the artist had been in, barring parents', a double bed. They had a cup of coffee and sat rather awkwardly on its edge, by the built-in bed table with its alarm clock and books. He put his hand on the artist's knee, and slowly moved it, quite knowingly, and in a back-and-forth motion, up the artist's thigh.

Things – unfortunately or fortunately, depending on what you were expecting – didn't go further than that. Neither of them pushed it further – out of propriety, inexperience, fear, boredom. The artist was both scandalised and proud of the interest provoked in The Who's *Tommy*, and was happy to leave it at that. He called a few times afterwards, but the artist did not answer. The artist had, in the artist's own way, run close – cut close – to a seam of difference that was unexpected: those open moments with other people, the forking-path moments that neither really control.

ADOLESCENCE The early years are the formative period in our lives – when tastes emerge, opinions start to be voiced and relationships forged. This was certainly the case for the artist, so it is with great relish I attempt to shine a light on the first act of this intriguing

biographical story. Contrary to popular opinion, the artist's first
ten or so years ran along conventional lines. Family life was stable,
friendships flourished at school, end of term reports were good –
if not spectacular – and there was even moderate sporting success.
But biographies, like lives, need key moments – episodes that mark
a turning point and start us off in a slightly different direction.
I can't be sure the following story is a precise recollection of the
facts, but suffice to say as an opening anecdote, it more than serves
its purpose.

One Wednesday afternoon the artist was walking through the
school corridors. It was raining outside and most of the children
had gone home for the day. The artist was having an extra maths
lesson on account of problems with basic algebra. Mr Davis, the
teacher had become increasingly frustrated by the artist's inability
to grasp basic mathematical formulas so asked the artist to remain
behind. There were about ten minutes before the class began and
the artist was sliding down the corridor, pushing the holey shoes
along the floor with a fluctuating sense of boredom and delight.

Walking down the south corridor of the school, which on one
side looked out to the playing fields and on the other housed the
boys and girls changing rooms, the artist heard the sound of
running water. This was strange at this time – most of the children
had gone home for the day. Slowly, the artist opened the door to the
changing room to discover that the water coming from the shower
had dripped to a halt. Creeping around the corner the artist caught
sight of a pink, plump, perfectly formed bottom. The body – it
was an adult for sure – was bent over as if picking something up
from the floor, meaning the view of this delightful behind was
picture perfect, as if on display purely for the artist's delight.
In that moment, the image of the bottom, with its curves, bulges
and simple lines, became etched in the artist's mind. But it wasn't
the bottom itself that the artist found so alluring. It was the act
of looking, of discovering – of a slightly un-hinged delight of being
in front of something utterly unexpected – a heady self-satisfaction
generated by the gaze of the artist's eyes. After what seemed like
an eternity, the artist suddenly became aware of time passing and
scurried out the door.

From that moment on, whenever the artist picked up a pen,
pencil, or later a paint brush, the first thing that would appear were

two semicircles side by side, joined in the middle. It became a way to kick-start the excitement that was felt on that autumn Wednesday afternoon and was a sign – or warning – of the potential of images.

THE ARTIST'S DRIVE He/she wishes to create and reproduce conditions, determined to pass on a sensibility to bloody-single-minded manipulation, even though he/she has chosen to live in one of the world's largest cities whose constant cultural production does not correspond with the length of understanding he/she experiences elsewhere (in hyper-aesthetic syndrome). There, there (naturally) is no more stability, and no less bloody-single-mindedness. Though what is absent there – besides language and reproduction (though it can be contained in language, it can) – are the effects of shifting external forces (such as language) assimilating your priorities and appearing entitled to your complete attention.

It seems easier to tell you this, he/she said the point is to pierce the veil of illusion and see underneath to the skeleton, to the infrastructure, to the plumbing, and see how this stuff is actually made and how the magic effect is produced. You can't live as anything other than history's fool if you don't make an effort to do that. I mean, he/she said you will always wind up being history's fool – it's not like you're going to get out of it – but the only hope we have is for people not to be literal readers, not to be fundamentalist readers, and to understand that, from the Holy Scriptures on, the whole point is to interpret and to understand. I think theatre forces you to do that. The great thing about having somebody die at the end of a sword fight is that it takes a lot of physical energy to do a sword fight. So they're dead, but their ribcages are heaving up and down. The incomplete, imperfect illusion will never be unnecessary for human beings, and its home will always be in the theatre, where everything, including death, is simultaneously, thoroughly and yet not entirely convincing.

THE ARTIST AND DRUGS Mooky heard the words coming out of a mouth that Jeff Koons wasn't really an artist, he was a Republican, but this claim hit the deck like a tonne of kitsch. *The Starless and Bible Group* met every fortnight in a small shop in Porto that was sparsely decked out with experimental pamphlets and records. Staring at the out of focus face of a rabbit with stars for eyes, Mooky was starting to feel that collaboration was not the right genre. 'I think like a genius, I write like a distinguished author, and I speak like a child', Nabokov was supposed to have said, but like many a fuzzy artist before – Mooky tried to work backwards – using this quote as some kind of mathematical formula – hoping that, speaking like a child, might, therefore, mean thinking like a genius. This was hard even for Mooky to believe.

Pool, with an album sleeve square of Frank Zappa behind him, had been applying the same formula to abstemia, and hatred of hippies, with much greater success for his self-esteem. It was a popular topic in the group and one that fuelled a dress sense avoiding any hint of kaftan or excess hair. Cuts were sharp, tailoring didactic and music, as much as possible, synthetic.

'Koons said that he was using art like other ethnicities might use sport – for social mobility.'

'That's genius!'

'Yeah, if you're eighteen. I am those 'other ethnicities' he's talking about.'

Reflected in a Uriah Heep cover, Mooky started to spin out on Pool's distorted face – watching it drip into itself whilst the group argued over the branding for their non-existent product. They had met at art school. Very early in the second term, Mooky had entered their empty studio after a morning lecture to find Pool slashing a painting of women floating on their backs in a lake of milk with a flick knife. Not being familiar with the process of 'negging', Mooky was powerless to resist Pool's strategy of seduction – and became involved in an unfamiliar game of sex chess. Pool loved James Bond, Charles Bukowski, Henry Miller, wrestling, Andy Kaufman and the idea of murder. Two years later and looking at this reflected face – mercurial and a puke of colours – Mooky wondered what Pool would look like, chopped up into bits of meat and arranged in a baroque bouquet of flowers on a mahogany slab. Mooky was hopelessly in love with Pool and even the dismembered body

Page 14. </Colleges/etiquette of reports/guidance1:45/c.>

and furthermore has obvious implications for confidentiality, but if dealt with with intelligence should be possible: extracts from example below.

NOTES FROM A PEDAGOGIC PSYCHOLOGIST'S REPORT

The subject was one of 5 student volunteers from an art programme of good repute to a diagnostic experiment to ascertain the experience of art students, in a subject area generally advertised as being characterised by freedom and open-endedness.

Session 1: Subject is enjoying the early stages of the course, though expresses some uncertainty as to the group discussion format, which seems hit-and-miss as to whether topics are pertinent to any given student's concerns. Subject understands that this is probably inevitable, but nevertheless experiences a wandering mind and is not sure whose problem this is, simultaneously finding it difficult to forget that fees for partaking are tediously earned by an hourly-paid catering job; and that therefore the programme is, likewise, difficult not to measure by the hour. Try as subject might, these thoughts encroach, in spite of an awareness that they are supposed to be irrelevant; and the more subject reaffirms that to dwell on such factors is to compound the problem, the more enmeshed subject inevitably becomes. Subject can see this leading to questions of whether this 'irrelevance' is really the case, and eventually to thoughts which undermine any ideas of art being 'disinterested' and 'above' such material concerns, towards how such notions are in fact politically questionable and may even act as a smokescreen - even in a forum in which 'politics' are regularly discussed, with palpable piety and enthusiastic idealism.

Session 3: Subject has become attentive to the point of obsession with the power dynamics within the group; specifically the way in which, under a broadly 'liberal' consensus, apparently disinterested and objective debates are shaped to appeal to the centres of power in the dynamic, the tutors. Subject is fascinated by the motivations this reveals (subject enthusiastically participates, to subject's own bemusement), and by the levels of conformity, obedience and conservatism thus variously illustrated. Also, it is commonplace for students to think and talk about the programme itself, rather than upon what in theory should be the whole point of it i.e. the art that is made. This all applies also to individual tutorials, which in many ways are far more revealing, both of the tutors' self-regard, and their convenient presumption of the neutrality of the discussion in terms of power. This is increasingly amusing to the subject with regard to the frequent earnest discussions around political responsibility.

Session 6: Subject felt an inward disagreement with what a tutor was espousing about subject's work during a tutorial, but felt unable to give voice to the objection. In fact, subject remained silent, full of self-disappointment at thinking better of disputing the point, simply because the tutor had in their control subject's mark in the upcoming assessment. Or rather: this feeling arose in later thoughts about the tutorial, whereas in the moment subject had made the decision *instinctively*: and this was the thing subject found most disturbing of all. Subject is thinking of leaving the programme.

Session 9: Subject's artwork has been receiving a lot of attention from galleries, curators etc, with a sharp upward direction in professional profile. This is a source of great gratification, as like most artists and art students, subject has been making work for years with little or no attention. What has struck subject most forcibly, though, is the effect this is having upon the tutors, who seem visibly conflicted in spite of crude attempts at disguise, their reactions ranging from 'subtly' increased harshness in manner, to hints of a kind of sneering - as if subject had betrayed some agreement or other, to do with, subject presumes, 'integrity' or 'disinterestedness'. This is perplexing: subject can only think that the attitude stems from some idea that there are different kinds of success, differently valued, and that the version subject is experiencing is somehow the wrong kind. This judgement seems a moral, even hypocritical one and rather disgusts subject. Subject asks whether the attitude is a 'recognised psychological compensation strategy', to be found in any institution - in this case from tutors made uncomfortable with a worldly success they themselves crave; and regardless of the fact that the programme they teach on is advertised as enabling exactly this success. All this has amazed and profoundly dismayed subject, especially re: power dynamics; and further increased growing doubts about the programme, which subject has begun to think is founded upon false premises.

</Colleges/etiquette of reports/guidance1:45/c.>

offered some sort of hope towards selfless pleasure.

'He's the last thing you'll see before you die,' shouted Lower.

'Noooo,' the group bayed backwards.

'You can run but you can't hide.'

'Awful – don't say the first thing that comes into your head – never.'

'Eight legs, two fangs, and an attitude'

'That's good'

'Arachnophobia'

'We've got eight legs'

'And two fans'

'We've got attitude'

'That's almost all we've got,' thought Mooky.

THE ARTIST'S ONLY LOVE The artist's fourth marriage was met with trepidation. The previous three had not ended well, and both family and gallerist felt the new attempt was unnecessary, particularly at this stage in a career. Urging the artist to exercise a degree of pragmatism, and recall previous heartache, they evoked the marital traumas chronologically, in the hope the artist might see sense.

The first, they said, had delayed an artistic breakthrough, keeping the artist rooted in Horsham with Steve: captain of Brighton and Hove Albion FC. Untravelled and susceptible to small-town heroes, the teenage-artist fell firstly in love, and secondly into a marriage, structured around Steve's training and interests in pub quizzes and pie nights. With an untameable wheat intolerance, and no capacity for facts, or sport, the artist became disillusioned with life, and the marriage was annulled within a year, on account of 'absence of things in common'.

The second, a decade later, was more practical – allowing the artist to extend a stay in San Francisco, and continue a journey of 'self discovery'. Long-term prospects arrived with Santiago, whose Latino genes and US status captured the artist's heart. The result was a whirlwind wedding, followed by teary breakdown, when the artist realised marital life was distracting and the search for 'self' had ceased. This rendered San Francisco redundant, breaking the artist's heart as much as it broke Santiago's, and the decision was made to return to the UK for a focused journey of art production in London.

This decision carried the artist promptly into the arms of Sergei: a Russian art collector. Their eyes met across an Anish Kapoor in a crowded art booth, and it was, again, love at first sight. Handsome and heavily perfumed Sergei seemed promising to everyone, with the artist's gallerist especially enthused. Sadly the relationship deteriorated, post nuptial, when Sergei's obsession with sellable art production and fluctuating oil prices began to rule their marriage with an iron fist. The artist's freedom of expression felt pressured, so the artist ran away, to become productive under less personal/ professional confusions, divorcing Sergei online and moving to Greece.

Armed with only an art kit and the *Rough Guide*, the artist spent a year moving from island to island, eventually meeting Yannis on a ferry to Athens. Three times world backgammon champion (currently ranked third), tanned, shirtless and with his own mandolin – the artist succumbed to the Greek. He responded well, taking the artist to his family's beach bar on Mykonos, where they set up home in a flat above his mother, aunt, and three brothers. After several weeks of orthodox inter-family feuds, it was decided that should the artist stay with Yannis, a Greek wedding was in order.

Family and gallerist responses arrived promptly, via hotmail, begging the artist to consider these tough economic times and the importance of retaining focus. Emotional distractions would not be helpful, they said, but really, it was too late. With post-lunch highs of 30-plus degrees and a late-morning shift at the beach bar, the artist had relaxed, and the warning lay unheeded, in an inbox of unanswered curatorial invitations. And so they were married, and the artist became a Mykonian Papadakis.

By morning the artist would swim and make cappuccinos for the tourists. In the early afternoon the artist would sleep, waking in time for spectacular Greek Island sunsets, which were painted in water-colour and sent to the gallerist, to sell in the art fairs, and hang in his kitchen.

The marriage continues, happily and successfully, today.

Artist L always considered their greatest achievement to be the fake exhibition *World Wide Proletarian Revolution with Unlicensed Pleasure as its Only Aim Comes to Shanty Town*. The work didn't exist in any real physical sense, it was pure guerrilla theatre, although the critics who wrote about it didn't know that. The exhibition was allegedly staged in an obscure rural location with the art works destroyed at the end of the show. The non-existent paintings that L had supposedly made were described in some detail in a press release accompanying an invite to the exhibition. The same text explained that the pictures could only be viewed over one weekend, and on the Sunday evening all the work would be destroyed as a protest against the commercialisation of art.

L had the invites and press release ready to go to press for some time before they were printed. That said, since the artist was living through a time of strife they didn't have to wait forever for a postal strike to take place. The dates for the show were made to coincide with the strike and by bribing a postal worker the envelopes containing them came to be stamped with a date just prior to the strike (although they were actually posted once the strike had been brought to a successful conclusion). All the important critics in L's country of residence received the invitations after the non-existent work had allegedly been destroyed.

L had for some time been leading a double life as Y, an important newspaper art critic. Critic Y seemed quite different from Artist L but this was simply because Artist L was a master of disguise. When Critic Y wrote a glowing review of *World Wide Proletarian Revolution with Unlicensed Pleasure as its Only Aim Comes to Shanty Town* under the headline *Free The Genitals, Cage The Generals*, many other critics felt compelled to review the exhibition too and to do so they had to pretend that they had seen it. There was much debate in the press, and even on the radio and television, about the paintings in which L riffed on the idea that a communist revolution is sexual in nature or else it is nothing.

While everyone admired the carefully controlled brush work in L's paintings and mourned the destruction of those shown in

Summer '58, Albania

Friends visiting after a long bus trip

'Bloody-single-minded manipulation'

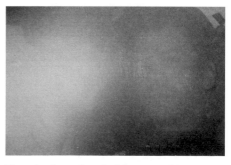

The only picture found of the artist when in Russia

New York, 12

Where he was found floating

The artist lived for a long period of time
in this hotel after their house was burnt

Leading a double life

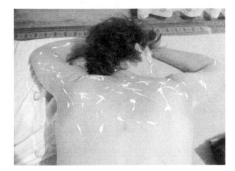

A time of strife

The artist's mother

The holiday cottage in the distance

The entrance of the tunnel

'Anyway I must confess I do not recall leaving that night or indeed much else'

Jacob

The tragic event

The beloved dog

It happened under that sign

The feeling of being upside down
was too great

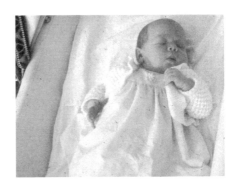

'Burying always presumes that someone else will dig the
offending items up. Maybe that was what L hoped...'

Mr. and Ms. O'Connor

'History's fool'

'Freedom lies in normality'

On their fifth anniversary

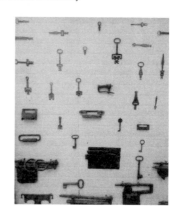

World Wide Proletarian Revolution with Unlicensed Pleasure as its Only Aim Comes to Shanty Town – there was much disagreement over whether the works were pornographic or simply erotic. The critics based both their praise of the aesthetic merits of the non-existent pictures – and their diverse views on their hardcore content – on a mixture of L's extant work, each other's reviews, and of course the descriptions of the fake show in the press release sent with the exhibition invitations. The more conservative critics, many of whom loved L's deployment of photorealism, were appalled by L's exhortations to fuck in the streets for proletarian victory.

When the controversy over *World Wide Proletarian Revolution with Unlicensed Pleasure as its Only Aim Comes to Shanty Town* finally died down more than six months after the non-existent exhibition made its debut in the media, L issued a press statement explaining that the exhibition of paintings had never taken place and that the real work was the prank that L had played on the critics. Those critics who had been taken in by the hoax were incensed and dismissed L's work as absolute rot, but the younger critics who were finally able to get their reviews published when editors sacked writers who'd claimed to have seen a show that had never taken place, hailed L as a genius. L, of course, denounced these supporters as careerists who would praise anyone and anything that provided them with personal benefits. L, like all other practitioners of relational anti-aesthetics had no time for critics or curators...

TRAVELS The artist only ate canned food for the five years preceding the now infamous Biennale show. This was not, as was famously assumed, an artistic or political gesture, it was simply a personal challenge that turned into a kind of habit. In this way it was similar to the artist's tendency to hop occasionally on slab pavements, or only wear clothes bought in years that ended in even numbers. Like the hopping or the clothes, these eccentricities, once noted, became mistaken for artistic practices, though never so publically as at the Biennale.

These habitual and repetitive rules by which the artist lived are
in fact well documented, and though they seem bizarre and even
frivolous by most OCD and autism spectrum standards, are most
likely to have been related to them. Certainly they score low on the
Yale-Brown Scale, and tend not to fit the standard obsessions such
as hand-washing and hoarding. This is largely because the artist
seems to have been happy to change these quirks or challenges at
will – to happily stop one habit and start a new one. It is probably
this and the fact that so many of the artist's works used repetitive
and performative strategies, that has lead people to assume that
these habits were also part of the artist's practice. The artist's work
that year at the Biennale, for instance, was to sellotape a single
common fly to every public-facing door in the city.

The artist's reaction on receiving the Biennale's Prix D'Or is well
documented, and indeed has been critically applauded. While the
flies had largely gone unnoticed, the selectors, critics and popular
press had fixated on the artist who constantly carried around a
rucksack of tinned goods and an opener. The best restaurants, at
first put out by the appearance of someone refusing their food and
eating instead from tins, started to court the artist as fame spread
from art journals to tabloids. The warmest welcomes along with
the best (and most conspicuous) tables started to be reserved.

Largely unconscious of this growing reputation (fuelled by never
reading reviews in the press), the artist was pleased at the attention,
bordering on adulation. It was only at the prize ceremony itself
that it became clear to the artist that it was the tins, not the flies
that had earned the Prix D'Or. The barrage of tins hurled at the
judges has gone down in history as a critical milestone in political
performance. Much has been made of how the first (opened) tin
to be thrown was alphabetti spaghetti. The disruption to the
ceremony, and angry storming-out were warmly received (though
some critics felt that the over-dramatic theatricality of the gesture
played too much into the popular press, and was unrealistic).
The artist's subsequent public denials were equally well received,
and the artist's leaflets refuting the canned food work now
command high prices at auction.

My dear I, It was a joy to see yo name
in my mailbox, but I'm not sure I can help you regardin your
business. The last time I saw L, I am certain I was rather pigeon-
eyed by the time I left, and have consequently rather disremembered
myself from what was said that night. A smudge of a memory!
I shall try to relate those small moments I do recall. You already
know things were delicately stewin between L and me some years
prior, yes? Well, we appeared so pleased to see each other at first –
it had been such a long time without words. But, when the eagerness
had slackened from our conversation – when the food had reached
room temperature, both cooling down and heating up in equal
degree, with only a single chicken wing lying on a pool of gravy
in the centre of the table – L got up to put on a spoken word record.
It was decided for us both that what Ms. O'Connor had to say
(L had always had a southern gothic bent what with L's mother
passin through Milledgeville at the time of conception), was clearly
better than any verbiage I would musta that evenin, and so,
together, we put our knives over our forks and bent an ear to the
violent and their terrible affliction of bearing away. I wondered
whether L's record selection was a tacit acknowledgement of our
own times together, affirmed in the breathy accent of dissent.
It was never mentioned explicitly.

We had hardly spoken since ten years prior, durin which time
L had taken up with a man named J (perhaps your research has cut
him a rather fine figure already?). Reading between my own badly
delivered lines, J was the leadin character throughout the decade
of my absence as L's friend, confidante, lover and muse, in no
particular order (I'm shure L gave them equal merit). It was unclear
to me, durin dinner that last evening we spent together, whether
J was away on business, had died prematurely, or was, in fact,
upstairs, havin no inclination or, indeed, ability to socialise. I
thought it may indeed be the latter, due to the fact that, havin
made the wrong crossing to L's bathroom durin a rather more
ambient section of the record (a visit necessitated by three bottles
of Slovenian white), I happened to pass by an operatin oxygen
pump. Its tubes were speckled with condensation and they snaked
their way up the stairs and under the door of what I presumed
was a bedroom. Returnin to the dining room to finish up Ms.
O'Connor's finale, I could not help but notice that the pauses in

her clipped narrative were punctuated by the mechanical sound of compressed air percolating through the artificial lung.

For the same reason it is impossible to discuss Robert's bad breath at Sally's funeral, J's absence fell into the category of unmentionable that evenin, though I witnessed him in an emblematic sense. A digression, if I may, though maybe you already know this: L told me they met in California when L was stuck without a driver's permit. L still had that well-paid job cooking meals three times a day for the pet dog of that sawbuck actress. J, in possession of a state license, was the driver for the dog. I do remember L showin me some drawings from that time – very influenced by J. Not least because some were sketches of him, but mostly they had that vertigo feelin that L had been cultivatin in the work since New York.

Anyway, I must confess I do not recall leavin that night, or indeed much else besides the measured wheeze of the machine in the hall. Please keep me in mind when you complete yo research. I am old and my memory is as reliable as my spelling, but if you think I might, then do let me know if I can help. And though I feel I have said nothing at all, I now ask questions of L myself, feelin a little sad that I had not thought to ask such questions durin our time together. Please send me a picture of yo research in the Pullman Library. The Woolf's collection muss be exquisite.

Yours aff,

P.

*

AUDIO TRANSCRIPT OF RECORDING INTERVIEW WITH J – MARKED FOR DELETION. NB: FAULTY. LEFT MIC (INTERVIEWEE'S LAPEL) NOT WORKING.

I: Could you tell me a bit about how you first met L?

J:

I: [laughs] I corresponded with P recently who mentioned to me that L had taken a job as her canine chef. Was that because L was a fan of those films? They certainly seemed to have influenced L's

works from that time in Los Angeles, in a satirical manner if
not entirely the source material for the avatar that L used during
that period.

J:

I: Yes. It seems a better idea to burn than to bury such things.
Burying always presumes that someone else will dig the offending
items up. Maybe that was what L hoped would happen around
now: that I'd go digging.

J:

I: L noted quite late on that things sticking around was a concern,
and spoke of wanting to either be present to explain them or else
these awkward souvenirs should vanish into insignificance. I
wondered whether you knew about some of L's influences then?

J:

I: I'm not sure. Was L the one who dryly noted that Bruce Nauman
had 'such scintillating ideas'?

J:

I: Yes, I can see in some of that early colour work that there is some
resonance. On a related note, do you think your work had an affect
on L's?

J:

I: There was a move towards more explicit references afterwards.
It all seems less veiled. I heard that L would collect anecdotes from
jobs, friends, from things you'd overheard. Which suits L perfectly
in a way, this kind of magpie behaviour with other people's voices,
accents and styles. A piratic attitude.

J:

I: It's interesting to hear you felt it was a contributing factor. And I understand it was becoming an increasing problem by that point? One researcher told me not to bother making an appointment with L after 2pm and never meet in a bar.

J:

I: Thanks. I'll send you a copy before it goes to print.

*

[Sender's copy telegram found tucked between leaves of *Enough Rope*]

P. I CANNOT EVEN LOOK YOU IN THE VOICE TODAY SO DON'T BOTHER CALLING. I AM NOT ANGRY BECAUSE OF WHAT YOU SAID LAST WEEK THOUGH I WISH YOU WOULD SUPPORT MY DECISIONS. BUT ANYWAYS DO NOT CALL ME AS I HAVE SNAPPED MY TWEETY SINGING WITH J IN THE BAR. MY SHOW OPENS NEXT WEEK. COME. YR AFF L.

*

[Transcription of a shopping list posthumously found on L's fridge, presumably unbought]

Dried mango
Gin
Vermuth [sic]
Tonic?

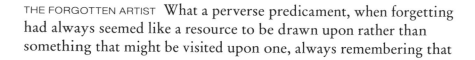

THE FORGOTTEN ARTIST What a perverse predicament, when forgetting had always seemed like a resource to be drawn upon rather than something that might be visited upon one, always remembering that 'dead sea of night and forgetting' which Nietzsche said was the birth of every artwork, in an essay first read back when artists citing Nietzsche was already rather passé, but which secretly always seemed like a sound philosophical alibi for a broad range of lapsus which might extend to not calling mum on her birthday, forgetting in any case figured as the metaphysical blinkers which allowed one the focus to make an artwork, in the same way that a cloister supposedly allowed a monk to forget the world-at-large in order to better focus on its salvation, that of course being an analogy which led to even more snickering than the Nietzsche (and probably, on reflection, quite rightly), so the best thing was normally then to invoke Karl Lagerfeld ('I keep no archives of my own, no sketches, no photos, no clothes – nothing! I am supposed to do, I'm not supposed to remember!'), but regardless: forgetting had seemed *useful* when it was one's own and it was only possible very incrementally to notice the effect of other people's, perhaps registered for the first time merely in the slight pique of not appearing in a young and meretricious academic's account of that artworld social set which twenty (or at least thirty) years before would have been referred to with a kind of synonymity, then the year-by-year experience of the ignorance of students to be discerned as much in their postures in class as by the fathomless indifference in their eyes, or a group photograph in *frieze* with the wrong name somewhere in the long caption, or the hardening of that expression on the artist's own face of mortified pride in hearing from yet another erstwhile peer that they had been interviewed by Hans-Ulrich, whilst also having to witness the process of curatorial strip-mining which had comprehensively recovered and revalued a clutch of indisputably minor contemporaries (or at least they had seemed indisputably so on those evenings downtown decades ago when they would always leave the bar early), and then the more common or garden indignity of an only averagely attractive Spanish artist who had been positively grateful that night in Berlin not affecting to not remember but *actually not remembering*, all of which cumulatively might have made a lesser person (or a greater artist) bitter, but about which the artist latterly came to joke (not ungraciously) that the situation might yet be redeemed by making a final work out of an act of withdrawal, claiming this evanescence, like Lee Lozano's *General Strike*, or Thomas Bernhard's conceit of banning his own work in Austria after death, this last sometimes followed by the observation that life had in fact become rather like a German sentence in which the absence of a last auxiliary verb rendered meaning permanently provisional, until even these formulations were rendered moot by an involuntary forgetfulness in which even being forgotten was finally occluded.

DEPRESSION On a bedside table a book had been left opened, face down next to a glass of water, half-empty. He (H) leaned forward and prodded at the book, moving it across the wooden surface until the corner licked a puddle of water beside the glass. The paper's fibres sucked up moisture. Printed words distorted, unread. The saturation proceeded until the book was flipped over. With one hand H held the dry portion of the page flat while ripping off a wet, tongue-like strip with the other. The strip was rolled up and compressed into a pulpy mass between his fingers that then flicked it towards the artist who was sitting at the end of the bed. The wad of paper pulp hit the back of the artist's neck, slithered down the spine and fell off when it reached the protrusion of the coccyx. A dark areola began to form on the sheet where it landed.

As none of this action incited a response from the artist beyond the involuntary glistening of a narrow track of skin, H picked the book up as if to read. A quarter of the printed page was missing and the remaining paper was sodden and sticking to the unread pages underneath. H tried to figure out the missing words, but they were too many. Disappointment spread through his body. The damp book dropped from his hand. Facilitated by the synthetic sheen of viscose and polyester, H slipped down and on to the pillow where he turned away and closed his eyes just as the artist stood up, walked round the bed and climbed in next to him.

The artist pushed the book, forcing it across the sheets until it fell off the top of the bed, then attempted to follow it into the inappropriate space between the headboard and the top of the mattress. Wedged-in and inverted, the artist's face pressed against the headboard's puffy upholstered surface and eyes followed diamond shaped lines formed of fabric drawn taught into pleats, folds and crevices, all held in place by cloth covered buttons that sat like inverted nipples at the centre of the swollen domes, as if someone had forcibly poked them into their depressions with an aggressive finger and at any moment they could have popped out again. But they didn't. The artist's hand glided purposefully beyond the upholstery, along the underside of the headboard's wooden frame. It found a short strip of black gaffer tape. The finger nails carefully picked at the tape, then plucked and peeled it back to reveal a jagged splinter – a tear in the wood that formed a finger-length, razor-edged shard.

In a series of small twists gradually progressing to quicker turns the artist wriggled out of the gap and manoeuvred to the surface of the mattress from where there was a clear view of the back of H's neck.

The artist smoothed the strip of tape back over the splinter then sat up straight against their headboard that concealed an exquisitely formed weapon in the most intimate contours of its dry grain.

THE ARTIST'S SECRET In the days before mobile phones,
you had to go to a telephone to receive a call.
You came to the black phone
on my desk in the gallery office.
You watched and listened
and said almost nothing.

A couple of years later
I was asked to take you downstairs
to make a phone call.
I found the number in the phone book
and dialled it for you
on the slow Perspex circular numbers
of the big white telephone.
As it started to ring I gave you the handset.
There was a touch, barely a touch.
Or had I imagined the touch?

I thought of exhibitions, the openings,
as family gatherings,
a wedding or a christening.
I thought of them as something
from an unwritten folk history
half as old as time.
The possibility of finding someone.
Later they are a memory
the echo of past gatherings.

You taught us how to
make something of very little.
Almost nothing was enough.
The weeds growing on a bombed wall.
Neither of us said very much.
I could not sing.
That was perfect.
You wrote '...and anyhow'.
We both made the sign of teardrops
on our cheeks.

The cream wall mounted telephone
by the front door
rang about nine o'clock at night.
Someone ringing
and hanging on for
my voice but nothing.
Several times over the years.

Another decade.
Another telephone.
A hospital phone box.
A little draft
fluttered the pages of my book
to your number.
Death. I cannot come tonight.
'It is enough that I came.'
You are the artist's secret.

THIS TEXT LIKE THE SOUND OF YOUR VOICE WHEN READING THESE WORDS

THIS PAGE
IDOLISES YOU

THE ARTIST'S WORK

Early Works and Influences

The Dark Period

The Artist's Secret Bottoms

The Studio of the Artist's Grandfather

Materials of Interest

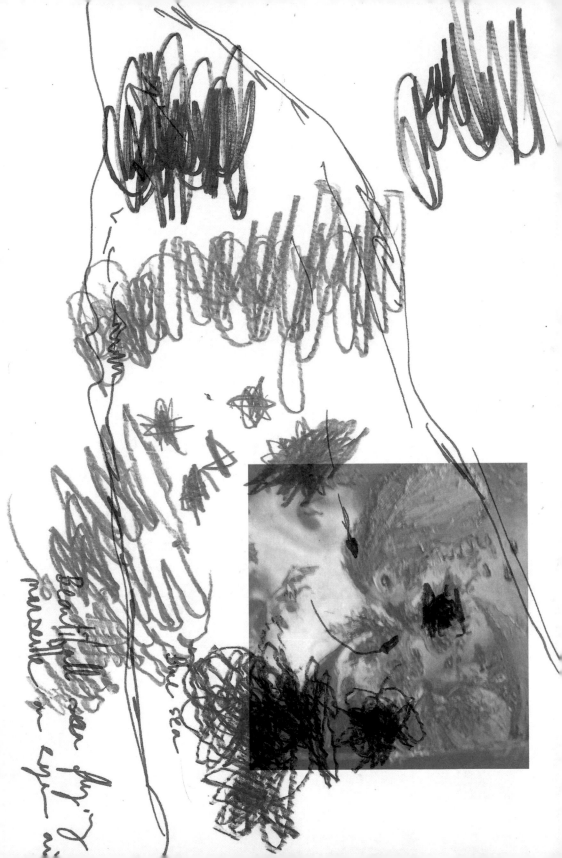

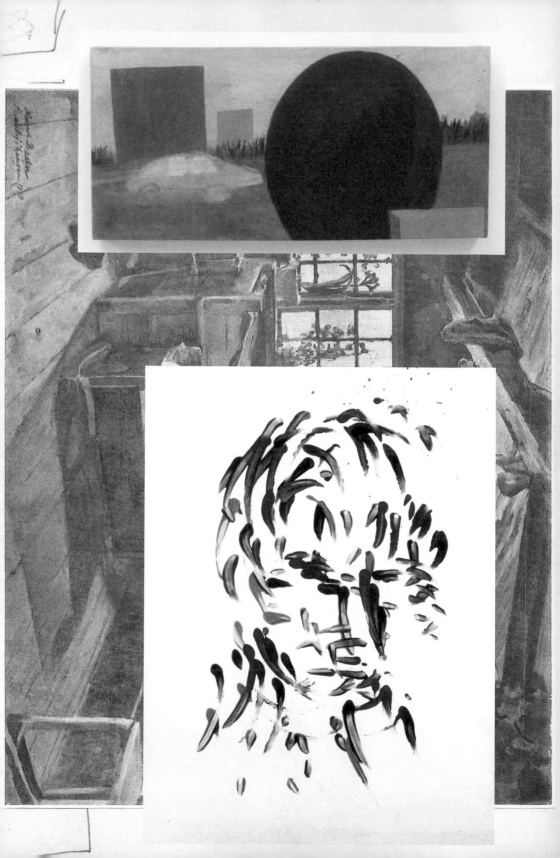

ouvirt -open / Ferme- closed

Beans +/all drawl you
want to grab in your hand,
harmorchenrichform both
cut into little piece like Bubble

FRITS THAULOW

graddad on h

— painting and sand slate
— painture gonflé / with
— morry pointing / on

This page is covered in very sticky and oily RED PAINT

(It is going all other your fingers, and get it allover this book by turning the pages)

FRA LYSAKER — FROM LYSAKER

NØKKEN — THE NIX

KITTELSEN

this PAGE TASTE
OF SWEET RASBERRY
iN YOUR
MOUTH

THIS PAGE IS WORRIED OF WHAT YOU THINK ABOUT HER

Insidout

make a table underreath

more pink HERE

Imagine someone with extremely beautiful hands is turning very gently the pages of this book for you

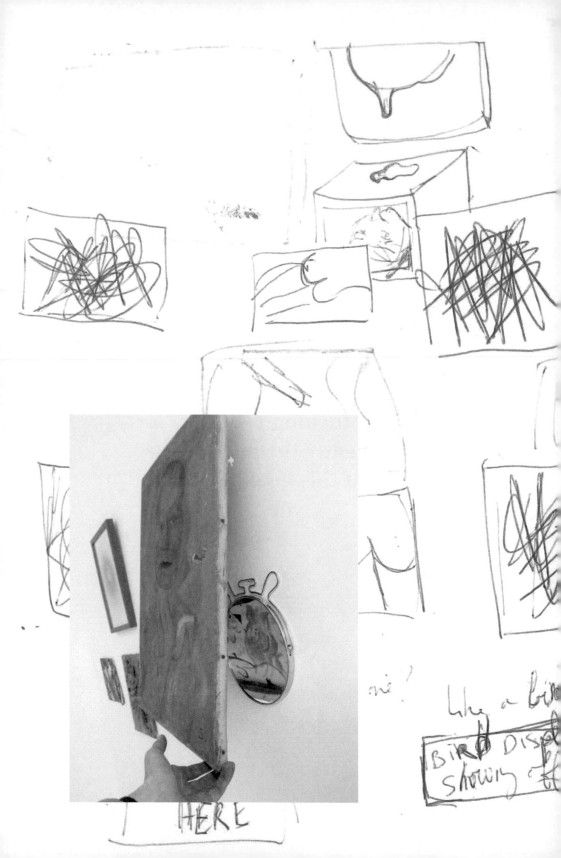

HERE

Like a bird

BIRD DISP[lay]
Showing off

ture
dropping on a monitor

push the wall
further

Red dripping

NO
HERE

-

ON THIS PAGE
THERE SHOULD
BE NOTHING

-

(go to page 55 now > (much more interesting)

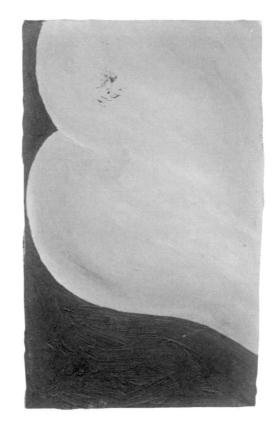

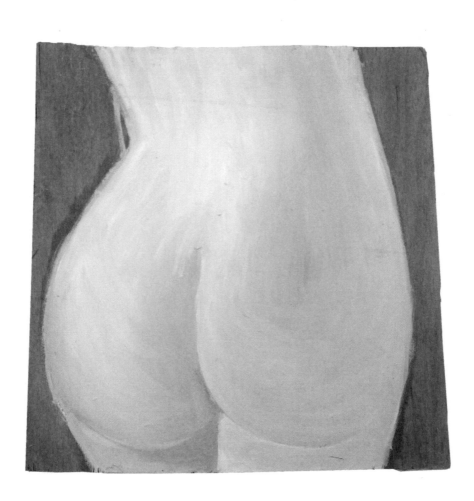

THIS PAGE
WISHES SHE
WAS BIGGER
THAN ALL THE
OTHERS

THIS PAGE
Thinks all The
OTHER PAGES
ARE USELESS

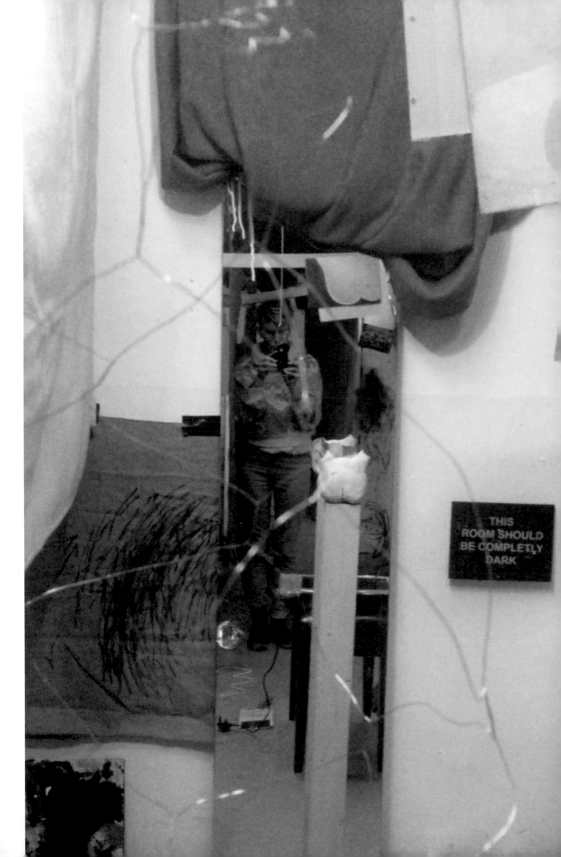

THIS
ROOM SHOULD
BE COMPLETLY
DARK

15 DAYS
WITH
NO FOOD

>>
This opposite page should be
green not blue
>>

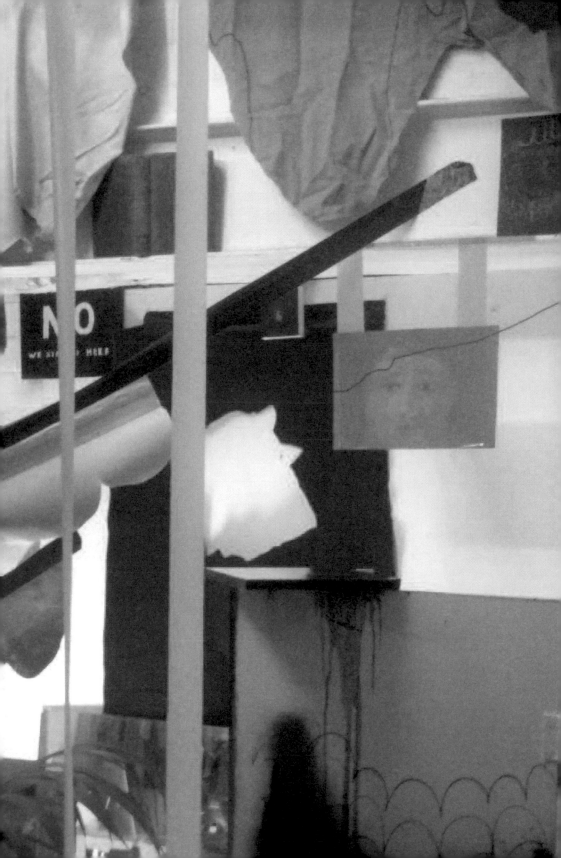

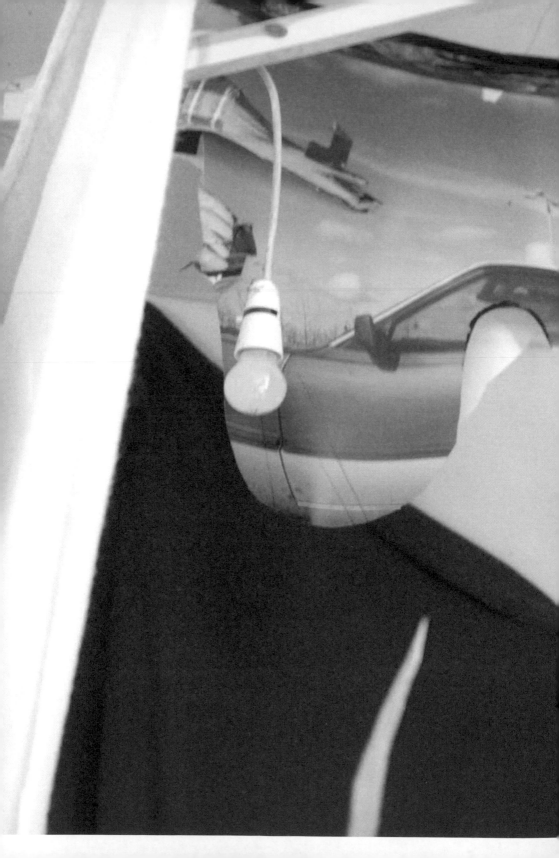

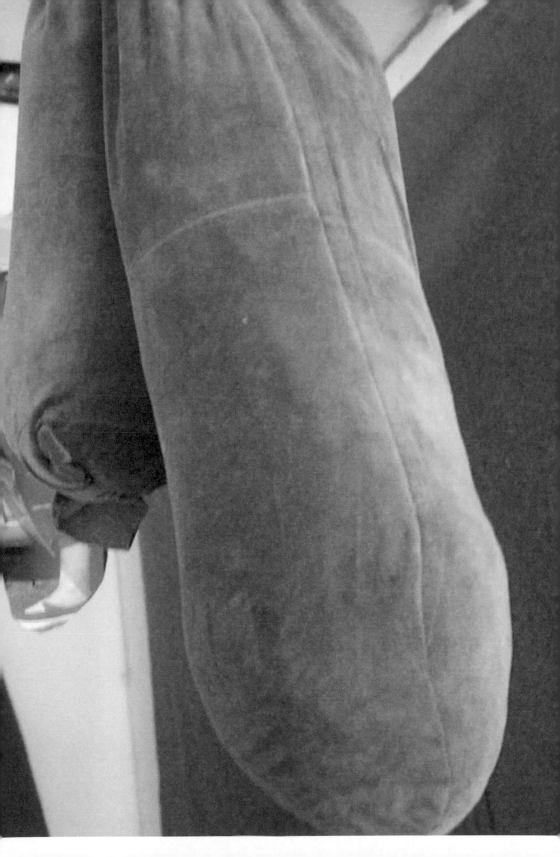

THIS PAGE
WANTS TO BE
THE MOST BEAUTIFUL
PAGE INTHS BOOK

THIS PAGE
WANTS TO
FLY ACROSS
THE ROOM

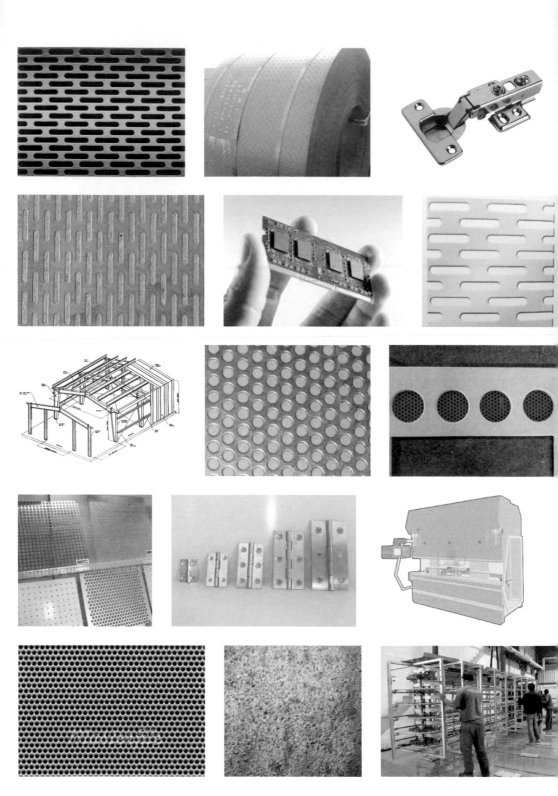

Dampening Roller

Ink Roller

Plate Cylinder

Blanket Cylinder

Impression Cylinder

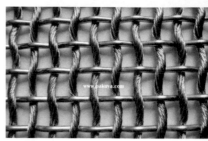

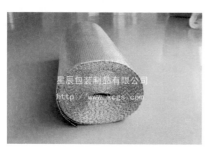
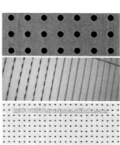

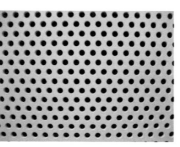

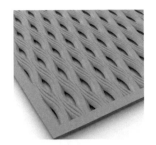

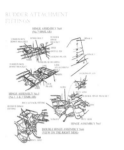

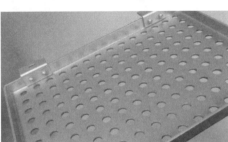

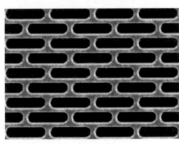

FIG.1

IDEALLY THIS
PAGE WOULD
HAVE BEEN
SEEN EARLIER

THIS PAGE
IS SO HEAVY
TO TURN

CHAPTER 3

BACKWORDS

Eight Responses

Backwords

Exhibition Documentation

The Grandfather's Influence on the Artist

Personal Communications

Lists and Scripts

POLICEMAN
Hakim Sadouk

Passion, love and violence are all portrayed in IT, HEAT, HIT. As a police officer, what springs to mind when watching this video is how close and yet different these three words can be. The photos and the video sequences take you from one dimension to another in an instant. The film moves from peaceful and calming photos, to sexy scenes, then to violent and abstract photos, all while playing a well-adapted and executed music track accompanied by the soft voice of the narrator. This is the type of pattern one sees over and over again in a domestic incident: love is followed by violence, then immediately by passion, but not always in this sequence.

The image that sticks most in my mind is the carrot being chopped in half. It is a powerful statement that expresses the amount of passion needed to commit any act of extreme violence. In this instance, it took a fraction of a second to commit the act, but maybe a long time to plan and certainly a much longer time to fix. This is the way crime is committed. The point of no return is what this act is about — the point at which reflection takes control, and not in a positive way.

IRONMONGER
Hikmet Savci

I liked the film. When I watched the flames I felt comfortable. It felt relaxing, like I was paralysed. The story is like a new galaxy, a new world, with nice sound and picture. It was a very good designer who put it together. When you're talking, you are taking people inside, you're listening to everything. You take the inside of the people. I can watch stories like this any time.

I think it would be good to show this film to everyone. It would be good to see it in the cinema, like an action movie. When I first saw the film, I saw flames, the seaside, people, a tray, water. Afterwards, I thought that you needed a different type of design, something Victorian, something old-fashioned, so I made the tray from metal, by hand.

NEUROSCIENTIST
Dr H Anne Leaver

Perception and Association of Visual Information in the Imagery of IT, HEAT, HIT by Laure Prouvost

S u m m a r y : The video installation IT, HEAT, HIT presents a series of visual images, accompanied by auditory and textual commentary, in a loose narrative. The perception of reality and experience is questioned, and the closest reality appears to be the response of the viewer to the video's images, either directly and readily interpreted, like 'heat' associated with the colour red, 'pain', associated with jagged images, or the examples of 'hit' starting with amputation of the viewer's leg, to the more elusive 'it', possibly associated with calm and the cool pleasurable images which predominate in the initial sections of the narrative.

A i m s : The question of reality and perception is raised at the beginning and the end of the narrative and at several stages during the sequence, for example the suggestion of rejection (eating the image). The narrative aims to suggest a series of experiences, including calm, confusion, disorientation, rejection, anger, and jealousy. There appears to be an association of colours, (for example blue, white and red), with mood, and of shapes with perception and experience (angles, edges, knives, needles, broken glass, pneumatic drill, smoke, compared with apple, trees, stone, feather, swimming frog, eggs, leaves, snow).

Structure: The viewer is invited to enter the narrative, stating that the individuals will not exist unless the viewer allows them to do so, by viewing the video sequence. It states that the viewer can terminate this existence by exiting after six minutes. However, this is the length of the full video, at which stage the viewer is asked to leave, suggesting that the narrative is also able to influence the observer. The sequence begins with calm aquatic summer images, of pond life and dappled shade, interrupted by a tree falling, and a sudden accident, which leads to a complex and violent climax. Image inversion is used early in the sequence, possibly indicating an early presentment of dissociation and disorientation. The 'hit' 'heat' sequence that ensues is associated with red, blood and percussive images and sounds, which are more obvious and immediate than the earlier, more diffuse, calmer images. The identity and reality of the characters, such as 'uncle', 'grandfather', and 'she', are more elusive and ambivalent. Most of the characters (with the possible exception of 'she') appear either hostile or unreliable. More than textual, verbal or

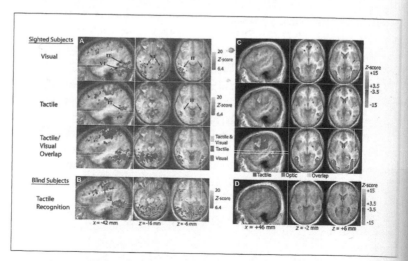

Neural response patterns in human brain, during visual and tactile recognition. Inferior temporal (IT) and ventral temporal (VT) regions are indicated. The bottom sequence shows areas activated by both tactile and visual perception.
Reproduced with kind permission of Dr Kupers and Prof Pietrini from Kupers R, Pietrini P, Ricciardi E, Ptito M 2011, 'The nature of consciousness in the visually deprived brain', Frontiers, 2:19.doi:10.3389/fpsyg.2011.00019s

musical commentary, it is the visual images that appear closest to deeper experience and to artistic expression, in variety and depiction of mood and experience.

Conclusions: The sequence of images and commentary in It, Heat, Hit, while commenting on the reliability of perception and interpretation of reality, also suggest a perception of experience that may reflect the response of the viewer to images, ranging from the more direct and readily interpreted (heat, hit), to the more elusive and diffuse, the ambiguously defined 'it' in the title. It is suggested that the latter may be associated with the pleasurable images in the earlier sections of the narrative. It could be argued that the more complex imagery in this sequence is more closely associated with artistic expression.

PRIEST
Father Rob Wickham, Rector of Hackney

The opening sequence of words, asking me to focus and give this short film your undivided attention, is very effective. Following these instructions, I was lulled into a false sense of security with the image of cooling waters that looked and felt so good.

The intensity of the music, images and countdown to the final minutes resembled scenes from the film *Ring*, which also included many images that bore no connection with each other on the surface.

I was being taken on a journey to places I recognised in Hackney, but also to the great unknown. I was left wondering who 'Uncle' was, I was left wondering who the five women talking about me were, I was left with the images of sharp knives, cut legs and breaking glass, all of which made me feel apprehensive, nervous and deeply unsettled.

SHOPKEEPER
Umit Seren

It's an unusual film, or documentary, and it shows lots of wild life and natural habitats of animals. Men hiking up mountains. It's a magnificent portrait.

PSYCHOANALYST
Bogdan Wolf

Artists have no need of psychoanalysis, so goes the prejudice, because they make no use of repression. Freud introduced repression as a mechanism that protects the subject from the trauma of the unspeakable real. So repression pertains specifically to the field of speech and language. When speaking, the subject appears to circumscribe the hole of the real, the crack in the body, the "one leg missing in the pile", as the film's narrator tells us. But to be precise, it is the signifier of this experience that remains repressed. There are experiences at the dawn of life which are unrepresentable because when they take place the language misses its target. Sexuality, satisfaction are also impossible experiences. Trauma is the language's failed encounter with the real.

In the experience of encountering a work of art, which should be distinguished from the subject's encounter with the repressed and unrepresentable signifier, it is the spectator who represses 'the real' of the encounter. The spectator wants not to know, and therefore wants not to see what he watches. This refusal is relative to the primary repression.

The laws of art, we could say with Freud, follow a different path, that of sublimation. In sublimation there is no repression. Can visual art be approached as a bridge between sublimation and repression? Can art succeed where the language fails? Or is the language of art subject to the same laws of the signifier. What is an image? It is a pure signifier. It stands alone, except that it in an associative sequence, connected to other signifiers by way of differentiation of form, shape, colour, size, sharpness. No two images are identical because no two signifiers are identical.

The film sequence unfolds, moving from one image to another, interlacing the image of the chopping of a carrot with the text "your leg branches out like a metal line going directly into your mouth", and the image of a boy jumping into the water with the sound of a shattering glass on impact. You must "eat the image", the narrator says. Eat your *Dasein*, Lacan says. Eat your existence, your language, live what you are made of, breath what you have been spoken to. But what is the sense of the boy jumping, the glass shattering, of the narrator suddenly gasping for air when an image of a dog and a text saying 'grabbed Mark's leg' appear?

The visual sequence is organised like an analytic session without an analyst. Interpretation remains unpunctuated and the unconscious is left to itself, to art. I will shatter glass into pieces in front of you and show you the soft feather, and the green frog spawning to life, and a naked woman holding a bunch of parsley, not over her pubic hair or breast, as we would stereotypically assumed, but over her belly, the mother's sacred place, and you tell me what I want.

The unconscious spits out the images, the narrator speaking all the time. It speaks about the granddad, the uncle who 'pushed the onlookers into the water', and the sizzling of the charcoal — 'it smells red' — red meat, a body, the uncle. Something went wrong, terribly wrong, and the scenes indicate this, giving us a warning. Something is always wrong, there are punches, smell of blood, and them, the women using sharp words, while the spectator witnesses a spiky, sharp ball and an apple with protruding pins and needles. There is a sound of a siren that strangely attracts us — like the ancient sirens Odysseus resisted — to the clingy sound of a car crash, shattered glass, again.

Tell me about my desire. What do I want in this? If the artist knows the truth of his or her desire it is in the sense of not saying it but showing it. Showing also means hiding, concealing, masking. But it is in the mask that we read what by concealing it at the same time reveals. The fantasy reveals what real satisfaction is at stake. The gaze is the axis of the visual encounter. Around it gyrate the spectator and the one looked at, and something else that slips away from this symmetry. The provocation of the gaze provokes sexual satisfaction. Being looked at is always enjoyed. It does not make sense, has no meaning yet, but is enjoyed, occluding, preventing, perhaps prolonging the refusal to know. The artist looks at the cars, frogs, feathers, cracked rocks, the sea, and they look back at her. In his youth, Lacan was once on a ship and the sailor asked him 'when you look at that can of sardines does it look at you?'

It is not by accident that Freud, who did not say much about the gaze, spoke of art as a representation of fantasy. The mother ('room full of men smoking like in your mother's room'), the granddad, the uncle, the women — we have a family scene where the father remains hidden, untouched, yet present in his absence. There are scenes of violence, punches, smashed glass, car crash and the determination of life spawned to continuation, as if wrapped up in the images, and lyrical moments of repose. The images support life, perhaps protect it. The unconscious, as a structure of language, remains at the back, knotting the paths of images that remain enigmatic, just as the mask remains enigmatic. At the end there is a lingering, meandering quantity of smoke. It is what remains.

GHOSTWRITER
Jane Gifford

Let go, and I'll catch you…
She let go.
He didn't. He didn't catch her. He laughed.
The taste of fear, the smell of disappointment, the sentence of missed opportunity. All in six minutes of snapshot staccato and searing solitude. We look on, we follow our instructions, we concentrate, we try, we try so very hard to comply and to trust what we are seeing and what we are told. Why do we trust? Why do we want to trust? Not simply want, we long to trust, to trust others we admire — with our emotions, our friendship, our need for love. But not uncle, whose sinister, creeping presence lurks without conscience — never trust 'uncle'.
The tree is sawn. The trunk topples. The words fall from the ceiling like a branch — with power and momentum — missing our feet, but not our stomachs that quail with the gut- twisting certainty of disaster that is so far beyond our control as mere spectators.
All these images, so perfectly and beautifully executed, with a precision and eye for stunning detail. Fingernail in walnut shell. Like dreams in Technicolor and stereophonic surround sound, building up the story of chase, and longed-for, long-promised escape.
Images and words. Words that are presented as images. White on black. Cling to them. They are the only safe forms. Again trust. I want more words in white because they tell me good things and they anchor my soul that is so badly in need of stability and relief from the horrid, screechy, angry, ugly images — just feed me more words.
Attempts at pacifying — with water and calm words — don't add up to anything more than further deceit. 'We will be nice to you now' is found to be a lie as aggressive as any amputation of leg or shattering of glass. We

live out our six minutes in the hope of better things to come — surely
good things to come; surely kindness is only a waft away and we shall
then relax and smile and clap and congratulate. But we are disappointed — we have jumped and not been caught and we suspect there
is much hurtful, acidic laughter.

THE BUTCHER'S WIFE
S Mely

First I want to congratulate you for putting
together a very interesting piece of film.
 It was very interesting how you described
 your words and put them together with the clips.
 Your clips were very sharp and clear.
 I wish you the best of luck for the future.
 This was not an ordinary piece of clip.
 I found it very very modern and different.
 It was quick to understand but you really
 have to concentrate and watch very carefully.
 Very different indeed.
            Good Luck

            S. Mely

This Page IS BORED

THIS IS A VERY IMPORTANT STATEMENT AND DEMANDS ALL YOUR ATTENTION

Ho! what a cake I made today,
what a cake I made today. It is a cake for my
brother's birthday. My mother tells me it is
not a real cake you only put the bread
up side down. I said mother you never trust me.
I made that cake and it looks lovely. A cake for my
brother birthday. Inside its full of surprise, there is only the
crust but inside the cake, I put a little bird, you can
imagine a little bird there picking some food.
My broher is going to be so surprise when he cuts the
cake, there will be a bird flying around us.
A bird with blue and yellow feathers.

the bread.

(out of the cake)

Blue around us.

This the cake my brother always wanted.

A very handsome guy with a lot of muscle told me
to meet him there in the middle of the see, he said
come and meet me there at 2pm towards the
horizin, i would be waiting for you.
I went at two, start swiming, swiming, till about
were he said, i kept going as i was not too sure
were, and i waited waited, swiming in circles for
hours as i was getting cold,
it was getting dark, he never came.

I love this red, i think we are going to paint our house this
colour we could not decide, red is my favourit colour, we
might paint the inside the same too.
The carpet is already red anyway.

I found some tape and though i should stick
it to the tail of Charlie my black dog for it to go
and find my lost grand dad in the tunnel he was digging.
So he could tangle him and bring him back.
But when Charlie came home he was all covered
of the tape, He did not find Grand dad
he could hardly walk, and breath.

I was so sorry for Charlie.
We had to take the tape off him.
His hair all came off, now he is pink.
Poor Charlie

I was just walking down the street,
and i saw this lady falling into a hole by roadworks.
A hole the side of her, about the size of a coffin but deeper.
A big truck was just about to pour in some tarmac, i could see the
tarmac going down starting covering her.
She started moving screaming and getting covered of the stuff.
I try to give her a hand but she did not want a help, she was very
angry, screaming, trying to climb by herself.
She manage to pull her trolley back up,
she was covered of tarmac, completly black now.
The trolley was full driping black everywhere.
She told everyone to move on there was nothing to see,
she run off down the street

My friends,
this is a picture we took after we went on
holiday by bus around the world ⟶ NO-ou
A night mare, none could stand one another,
scratching, pulling each others hairs all the time.
Never again, too much stress
although they look pretty inocent there.
To thank me at the end they made this huge painting
~~for me. i don't know what to do with it~~   it ~~is horrible~~ discus
~~if you want it you could have it.~~
~~Just call me we will arrange for delivery.~~

              told me
They ~~said~~ it was an interpretation of

      our trip, ~~and~~ ~~said~~ it
I would look great in ~~our~~ my next show. }
                              of us

                    ~~No one~~

I am very worried as i have seen this boat,
passing very very fast, with noone driving it.
you can see no one is driving it.
i am afraid it will keep going never stop and crash
into something, maybe someone
should try to stop it.
On the other side of the sail, there is a lovely
woman painted, from top to botum, in bikini. Very
naive but quite sexy, i wonder to who it belongs
to, it must be someone wife
that they love so much.

i wanted to show you my cat,
but he did not want to come
when i called him.

It was so nice our friends lend us their cotage for holiday. We had such a great time there place is so lovely, she had told me to be carfull at the vase her gran gave her, It was so upseting as soon as we arrive goerge with his ballon boke the vase staight away, i was looking in all the shops for the duration of the holiday to find something similar. at the end all i found was a blue square vase, i dont know what she is going to think, We had to more the sofa our cat is distoyed it, so i cover with nice indian sheets, the light bulb broke, mark had put some blue paint on the table so we though best was to make it nice so we made dots every where on the walls too it looked pretty nice.

[Handwritten annotations surround the framed text. Left margin, in French:] j etait syma de nos amis nous on preter leur maison de vacances. c'etait extra ... notre maison ... excellent ... charmante ... la photo ... j'aurai ... plus de ... beaucoup ... je ... love ... j'arrive george ... Bourbon ... route ...

Green Blankets

[Right margin:] the places we are staying looked a little Brit like this. But the floor was red tiles ... they was not sofas but chairs ... A present we thought we ... present then ... else the picture ...

taller + Bigger the walls ... were a strong pink the whole a lot Bigger

[Bottom, in English:] ... used the table to an ... piece of wood to ... the sofa But made a hole in the table / we have put a book on top But we glued to to the table i hope the wont realise with a Big chunkier ... the all big ...

In the morning i go to see them and sen to them a
little song. They love it as you can see.
i go like, hummmmmm, hummm, mumm, humm
humm.
at 9 am every morning.
I think every one should have a better life.

These vegatable feel from my cilling on to me.
I was just dreaming on a chair, and i got wake up
by these vegetable, falling hard on me. In the
ciling there is 3 holes now, i don t know how it
happen, now it is raining in my house, i thought it
must be a sign of god. I told my priest but he did
not believe me. He say i must be crazy, i told him
to come and see. Anyway he is a fucking stupid
priest. He never belive a thing i say.

This man really wanted to say hello to you.
He told me he likes you.
but you should see him now he has done his hair
blonde, he looks so cool a lot younger, he also has
a new nose. percing in the nose he looks so cool i
think you would like him.
He also mentioned a new buisness he is planing,
maybe you be interested in investing in it.
It s bulding a sky slope by famouse designer in
egypt.

Here i could not find the picture i wanted to show you,
it was the most amazing flowers, full of petal of amazing
diferent colour, there was just at that point a beautifull
butter fly, blue and green on it.
And in the back a tiger was just passing by folowed by its
little one and in the disctance you could just see a girafe.
I am so upset not to find it aany more.
I cant belive i lost it.

this light Bulb exploded

~~Yesterday~~ *when* ~~i broke this light bulb~~
a row egg fell from it,
~~I put it in my~~ frying pan.
~~I~~t was very good.

straight
into my

~~they loved eachother so much~~
a- The next day she was pregnant

b- He did bit her up later that night
she did end up in Hospital

A woman came out of this garage, completly
naked, and she was not skiny she was really fat,
she went runing, the fat was going in all direction
she went towards the milk man, jumed on him,
got him squashed on the floor, kissed him
everywhere and she ran back into this garage.
I dont know what sort of people live there, but the
guy could hardly walk after, he was limping very
badly. I think i am the only one to have seen it
happen.

for Bigben

Tou, Tou Tou
tou tooouuuuuu touuuuuuuu touuuu, touuuuuuuuuu
tou tou tou
touuuu touuuuu touuuu enfant de la patrie,
tou tou le jour de gloire est arrive...
tou tou tou tou tou tou touuu tou touu tou touu tou tou touu
touuuu touuuu, tou tou tou tou
tou tou aux armes citoyens,
contre nous de la tyrannie tou tou touuuuuu,
touuuuuu tou tou touuu!

trumpette,

£400 × 12 = 4000

M

Realy load Noise

everything
glasses
glasses / Radiation
£4500 the window

compatissante

This dog was making horse noise. i hear later tho
he was brought up with horses and not dogs. this
make sense.

When this man walk you can hear the sound of
money in his stomac, since he is small he he use
to eat coins. He also plays in band, jumping.

THIS TEXT SLAPS YOU TO KEEP YOU ALERT

GROUP SHOW 'MAY'

As you enter on your right you can see the first piece on desplay, wedding dresses made with exact proportion but all smaller, there is 100 of them for small people. The smell is stong of sweets mixed with the smell of polyester fabrics, a small black boy is walking around the place looking at you in a questiong way.

You are not sure if he is a child or a very small adult, he wears a black suit. You come out of this room turn left, you will see a window desplay of 15 pink ball, presented at an interval of 10 cm each, they seem to hold in balance.

Below an orange selertape line on the back of the shelf, it looks contolled and minimalist. As you enter on the cilling around 35 plastic football ballon and hanged in there as a floating clowd.

On your right a man with orange teeth is smiling. He scares you, he seems to have appear from nowhere... you are a little anxious of entering. Some bolls of strange fruits, on the level of one knees. You dont enter, on your right an other dispay takes your attention, bright coloured fabrics, folded in interesting shap as in restaurant napkins despay. 100 of different colour fabrics from africa, are hanged above your head, 3 people are talking together, hardly noticing you. You want to touch the fabric but not sure you are alowed. You think that some would look nice in your living room.

But you are in a show, on your left an installation of suit cases neetly presentend one next to eachother from the biggest to the smallest, brown to black. You wonder what the artist did mean with this display. You look up, a display of 15 stone sculptures of figures from the past are covered with fine net, you can just get a glimps of the feature of each personage as the net makes them look 2 dimentional.

You take a right and walk down a corridor, on your left is an open sky room, a man looks dead lying on the floor, he is not a replica, but a real person lying flat as if fallen from the sky. You get close he does not move but you can see that he is still breathing. You leave the room, take the 1st right and leave the show via the back entrance...

It is our second attempt to talk. This time it is a nicer setting though, much better than the tunnel. Although I don't understand how you can concentrate in such a place. Don't get me wrong: it is beautiful. Maybe too beautiful. I wonder if that's precisely the point: you demand our complete attention, but with such a pressing request that you constantly interrupt any possibility of grasping a uniform message, something that would disclose your real intentions.

Stepping away from the linear manner in which a narrative functions is essential; letting go of the established rules about how a storyline should be constructed is equally vital. A child may get stuck for half an hour on some very small detail of a story and not really get the whole picture. That's something I can definitely relate to.

So it is about not focusing, about forcing us to be transported by the visual and narrative rhythm you prepare so carefully for us, your audience. We are ready to consume your syncopated and yet well calibrated succession of interruptions. We are asked to make sense out of your stuttering messages, even when distracted by an overload of information that instead of helping us catch your objective, throws us back into a selfconscious perception of our viewing position. We are somewhere outside. We are just watching. Don't you find it too hot here? We could find a place in the shade, away from the loud music. It might be the rocking of the boat, but I'm getting a little dizzy here. Let's get straight to the point this time: an expanded idea of translation is fundamental to your work. I'm mainly thinking of translation from medium to medium, from language to language, from sense to sense. And you have used imperfections and intentional mistakes to underline the hidden beauty of the hiatus created by these constant transformations.

I am not feeling good either. Somehow I always get seasick, but it's nice to put a face to your voice. In most of my work there is no real beginning or end, just a constant movement of action and reaction. Small details might take on a disproportionate importance, and key narrative elements might pass unnoticed. I am interested in this flux of information where everything could be related to anything else, could be open to other solutions, other endings. The body of my work is totally intertwined: one work gets lost in another, the same shoot can be used for a complete different purpose somewhere else. All pieces are linked in one way or another. They might be sound pieces, performances or videos, and yet they can be translated into a painting, an installation or a video again. It is just another way to experience the same story differently.

Do I look pale? Would it be better if we ate something? They say the only way is to jump in the water. Maybe we should continue our discussion from there, otherwise we will be both sick soon. How is the water?

GROUP SHOW 'JUNE'

On the right coner is a red dot surounded with blue ligns it rought in texture from there you go down 4 cm to the right a little hand seems to be hanging a bapy hand, green, holding a large blue triangle, a splas of blue to the edge wright of the canvas. A ligne from let to right cross the image is made of thick paint, a photocopy of an old photocopy machine is hanged on the left corner of the image, in thront of it there is a plastic chair, and a big abstact form creamish taking the lower left side of the image, little spach of blue are dence in the bottom part deparated by about 3 cm each, the texture of the canvas can only be guessed. On the uper left over the photocopy of the photocopy... a sign of a cloud is pointed by the drops of paint, the vague rainbow of faded colour desapear in the botom right of the image. On the rigth 50 centimeter from the top and 5 cm fom the edge a ladder shape made of browny with blue edge curles to the lower left side where the creamish shape is, on top of all a bug splash of green turn into a tree is guessed, feet on branches, broken branches are seen at the bottom of the image, a guild licking an ice cream is looking up naively where a drop of blue paint is about to reach her face. On the pop side of the canvas a real plastic back is casualy resting... a metal poll is also hanged casualt towards the middle of the frame, the waight of it band the fabric inside. There is mark of paint by the floor just beneith it.

GROUP SHOW 'FEBRUARY'

A man have been seen walking around the exhibition covered of mud, just two eyes showing, we will ask you to be carfull, and help us make sure he does not touch the art work... he was hear to have come trough the garden as he was digging a tunnel from the uk and arrived here we had to close the hole as some of you could have fallen into it .

I woud like to tank a few people that made this show possible, the council of frankfort BP corporation, duch bank and the arts council of germany.

I think this show has achive tremenduous success, changing the gallery into a domestic home, as you may have observed on the left as you enter the gallery, the little table on the right should have been more to the left we appologies for this trouble. The large sculture by Peter Conrad has the presence that one could descrid almost transparent. It is such a pleasure to welcome you here tonight.

You may have missed its elongated legs could easly be miss concived for a wall. The very large and colourfull painting on the far wall, is an interpertation from the artist of a dog barking, I feel here you can understand end engage fully with the emaotion of the moment, this piece was actualy produced by my late grand father relativly known as a conceptual artist. He recently desapered as he was making is last work, this inclusion in this exhibition is an little homage to him and his home. I wont get in to this but... we miss him.

As you go upstairs you may have seen a few posters they are drawing that children had made in responce to this exhibions there senssitivity is uncany, this is a body of work that I feel strongly about, I forgot to mention, down stair to the right when you enter the little room just behind the stairs, the almost empty room here exhibit the most fine and descret wor of art of this exhibition. The waight of this little blue art work do get my heart jump. Every one say how busy they are how busy they are how busy they are we miss the little things we miss the space. As you are listening to my speech you might think... she is nervous or she is forgetting the most important art work of the exhibition. But I am talking to you about the work... maybe I will ask you not to look at me but just listen to my voice, I could be a floationg piece of clay mud... passing trought the art work of the exhibition and telling you about the work I could be your gide, ok just imagine I am just a little peice of mud floating going trought space and telling you what is what... maybe there is also a dog following me as I go through the gallery, the dog sometime try to snif your trousers and jump on you you push him away, we are here to look at the exhibition not an anoying dog.

There is a few point I need to point out and appologie on behalf of portikuss gallery. You may have also notices a whole in the wall we appologies this should have been refilled.

GROUP SHOW 'NOVEMBER'

For those of you who missed the show. Here I will describe the rooms, the show you have missed. First you take the first right, go down stairs, in the staircase there is a sound installation, a dog is barking at you very aggressively, a step is missing. You almost fall, at the bottom there is a mattress and a lady asking you if you are ok, you are entering a very large room, it's dark, 3 lights in 3 of the corners, by these lights on the floor a mouth talking, telling a story. On the otherside of the room a light is pointing at you following all your movements. The next room takes you to a bright pink soft room the wall and floor is soft. You come out the same way you got in. You go back up the stairs. Enter the first big room, here it's bright and there is only one thing on the wall a letter L. You cross the street, opposite, the big building host the biggest part of the show, you enter through two very big doors, going up, the first staircase is full of objects piled up covering lights switching on and off. Between garbage and object some pot of red and green paint has been thrown over the installation, a TV can be seen through with a face calling for help. You go down a very narrow corridor, if some people were passing you, you would have to stay very close to the walls to let then pass through. In front a small room with gentle music, there is a very large canvas, on its far right a big round soft red shape, from there a line going down to the bottom of the canvas. A silhouetted man lying on the floor a waterpuddle, 5 cm to the left a blue rectangle fading in the distance, next to it big splashes of thick oily light green, 4 cm to the left a light orange triangle, on the bottom right of the canvas is very messy cloud of spiky colours, some little red shape seem to be falling from the top left of the canvas towards the cloud, quite rough brush stroke, a face of a women with red lipstick about to eat the cloud, she is on the edge of the canvas, her hairs are floating in the wind. Some soft green, powder like, is gently sprinkled all over the canvas like rain, a little pile of it is on the floor falling from the canvas. In the next room, some text on the floor reading 'we are visual artists'. You take a first left two steps down, there are very bright big windows and a high ceiling. Here a projected video of a train passing going into a thick light greyish green cloud, disappearing into the light of the windows. On the left a wall covered with text you don't have time to read... the toilets are on the right, there you can hear some very loud classical music, they are extremely slick covered with mirrors, in big contrast to the rest of the show. As you come out of the loo, two people are fighting as dogs, on a ring full of hairs. A video conversation on monitor, one asks questions she tells she is doing a PhD, she thanks a lady called Pia. In the next room, there two people naked filming themselves, it smells of sweet you want to leave but the door has just closed behind you – you have to wait 5 long minutes till the green light – to leave the room. You leave the corridor is freezing at the end of it a series of very site-specific an awkward space that wraps round the back of the dramatic installations, examines the transient nature of public spaces. A flooded room, in the water a motorcycle seem to be sunk with still a flame coming out of the exorst. Next a room with six blown up photographs of chairs, you wish you could sit. On the side there is a plate on a small table where you are asked to make a donation. For this next space you find that the dimensions of the gallery are an exact replica of Westminster Cathedral full scale, chairs bolted to the walls and floors to replicate the seating arrangement. Room 29 is completely full of rotting apples, there is a donkey at the end of it covered with feathers in the same manner as a blue and yellow budgie. The last room a women comes towards you and asks you to follow her, she takes you into a room and kiss you on the lips, some shoes are flying around hanging on wires. As now machine sends snow into the room. If I were you I would miss room 6, room 70, room 12, all the same, room 16 has terrible work, room 32 is the cafe, I recommend the mocha. Room 17 is so unbearably noisy. Room 6 a good mattress to have a rest. Room 36 is strange, Guy, a warden in room 3 says hello to you rudely, first he could seem rude but he is the kindest person around. He tells you: you look beautiful, its part of an installation. Upstairs: an opportunity to see work by video artist TerCapu. An artist known for his fascination in psych and ema, Capu uses video to explore the ship between art, sub and view. Many of his films, like iva, made in 19 and 75's turned the tables on the viewer, polluting the situation so that the viewer became the subject matter. Between photography and cinema, he questions relationship with a poll planet. For more explanation read the text on the left wall. 4th room 6th floor: an audio piece transforms radio signals picked up from passing planes, satellites and amateur radio conversations into intricate projections and chattering in which car-shaped 'vinyl killer' record players and a miniature train create a quite din. On your right is the exit door.

IDEALLY ON
THIS PAGE WOULD
BE THE MOST
BEAUTIFULL
IMAGE

THIS PAGE
is LOST

THIS PAGE
IS SO HAPPY
YOU ARE
LOOKING AT
IT

MY GRAND DAD LAST
CONCEPT WAS TO DIGG A
TUNNEL TO AFRICA WITH
OUT BEING NOTICED BY
THE AUTHORITY.

He is out... the picture below was the jakets (thats the way he would hang it) he was wearing when we last saw him (my Grandma says that oftern there is things being stolen from the fridge, and once she found the computer turned of but still warm...) we just would like him back. Because you are here reading and you are interested in art... I though you may understand and be able to help.

I have been down a few more time recently to see if I can see him, but I have this very strange feeling every time I walk there for a few 100 metre I feel dissy starting to see all blue I feel like I am just a colour I become a blurb of blue and I can't really carry on, I still see a few packet of crisps there or then...

Grandad's jacket when he last left

But I though we should talk about this as someone earlier mention that they had see someone covered of mud walking arround rooms of a museum.

Kitchen dining room of Grandma and Grandad

173

Its been months in the dark, so he maybe a little confused and act strangly with people.

The trap to get to the tunnel my Grandad has been diging

It has been now two months that we can't find my gand dad, he just lives around the coner, just a few streets away, he is a conceptual artist and his last project was to did a tunnel from his garden, the idea was to cross the channel with out any permission or any thing it was his last project, its been years he has been working on it. With out any planing or any things, that was part of his concept how you can go against the legal system.

Wait used by my grandfather to open the trap

This used to be a sculptur of KS given to him

He started digging 6 years ago, he was very disciplined, waking up 7am every morning go with a little lunch my garn would have prepared he would always come back for dinner, but it has been two month now we haven't heard from he, my gran his very worried, she does not want to call the police or anything it would have been completly against his will, he would be really upset and it would distoy his work.

The other day she called me in tears she is getting very worried. I told her not to worry, I went to see her.

Grandad arm chair, the arm was made from a sculpture by KS that he did not know what to do with, so used it like that

The house is such a mess (here I took some picture for you to see), there is ground absolutely every were, the kitchen is full of hearth just the cooker are visible, to go to the garden you have to go by the bathroom upstairs its so full of hearth every where, the baths, I dont know how can my Grandma live like this, she was crying when I arrived. I told her, I will go down the tunnel and see if I could find him, she told me not to she was so worried, I had to push her away and clinb down the trap and

Car engine drawing – when Grandad was car mechanic, Sculpture used as tea towel hanger

Bounty Grandma loved, tea pats and cups she made for her friend – Wantee

The mess Grandad will bring back from the tunnel, and cisps he would take with him when going to dig, my Grandma only hate crisp too

enter the tunnel, I took a light with me it was so dark down there, very humid, slymy, I was turning into a ball of mud my self, the walls where so wet and I felt really stuck just enouth space for one persone, with a few pieces of wood trying to hold the mud away, it felt very glue and slimy, that why the living room is like this when my Grandad come back he bring so much hearth with him.

Portrait of Grandma by my Grandad, she really did not like it, She thinks she does not look like that at all

A sculpture used to repair table feet

After half an hour walking I could see a little table, with a few object drawing etc, picture of my gran when she was a young, cigarette, as I kept walking it is was so quiet, I could here drops of water, sometime

Sculpture used as reciept holder by Grandma

like the tube passing above, sometime the tunnel will drop sendently... after hours walking down there I was getting quite worried, I could see a few packet of crips here and

The place Grandma would keep the keys

there but no signs of him, I started screaming: Grandad where are you Grandad, where are you? can you here me? can you here me?

where are you? Grand DAD! GRANDAD!

After hours, I saw in the distance two small shiny white bals like eyes, I called Grandad even harder, but nothing and

Sculpture used as a brush by Grandma, she was trying to make use of all these object given to them by artist friends or that Grandad made

Short leg chair. Every time you need to move the chair you need to move the books too

177

KS sculpture used for sponge, it normaly stand straight

GD minimalist sculpture used as bin

no movement! I got so scared I did not know what it was, it did not move, I kept screaming: Grandad! Nothing, I passed the eyes but they where just two balls of clay painted... I was getting very cold and tired by now, at a point the tunnel was splitting in two tunnel, I did not know whish way to go, I though I should start walking back... I was very cold an feeling really down and scared in the dark like that.

Portrait of Grandad by Grandma or by Peter close relative

Friend KS sculpture used as door block

When I arrived back to the bigining of the tunnel, Grandma was there screming she had try to go down to find me but was stuck in the entrance as she is very big now, she just eat crisp, sins Grandad deasapered, I could see her leg moving

Eyes I found in the tunnel – new landscape desplay Grandma loved, so muchbetter that those eavy paintings she once had by artist friends

Tea service Grandma made for KS wife Wantee, Grandma admired her, she though she would like things in this style, but she always pretended to forget them, so my Grandma just kept them and we were forced to used them, its the ony things that she would keep clean from the mud. Just because she had made them

Lips cup made by Grandma

in the air, I had to push her out, she was very distressed and started shouting at me asking where have I been, I could see her head, through the tunnel, she screamed at me she said she was so worries, I said I was just trying to help, work back in I was friezing, she was shouting at me, in got so pissed of I left smashing the door at her, the door broke her nose...

Friend of family drinking from cup, its actually quite good as the tea has time to cool dow as it reaches the mouth

I was just trying to help... she can be so enoying sometime... any way we haven't heard anything from him still, it is getting very worrying...

Last week people from here said maybe they could help, so my Grandma came to meet them, she never lives the house, she is pretty big now, and climbing the stairs, she fell down, a step did brake, her leg got stuck, they ad to call the ambulance, she was so pissed of she did not want to speek to any one and left screaming.

179

More exemples of tea pot made by Grandma

Cup kissing by Grandma

Any way I just took this oppertunity as you are here reading, I though I should tell you any way, if you can help... maybe if you have seen him around he is pretty dirty, you can just see his eys really, some said thay my have seen him in france, we dont know we are very worried, if you know any thing please come and find me... she just lives around the corner.

Charlie the dog sculpture by Grandad

The next day I decided we should send our dog Charlie, to see if he could find Grandad, so we attached some tape to the tale of my dog and release more and more as he kept going... We ad to buy a lot of tape to release as charly was going down the tunnel at least 100 we would just add to each other and say Go chalie go! find Grandad, so he went ran ran, we were hopping he would just neet to tangle Grandad with the tape and bring him back, charly whent dow for hours and hours, he is not so tall but qite fast, its a black dog with lovely longish hair.

SO I TAPED THE TAIL OF MY DOG WITH THIS TAPE, SO I COULD RELEASE THE TAPE AS HE WOULD GO ALONG TO FIND GRAND DAD.

After hours of waiting we were getting worried but he finaly came back late at night all tangled wit the tape, all his legs wher tankle he could only walk with one leg now, he could hardly breath his tongue was dropping out, breathing very hard, he seend really stressed and tired, I tried to gently take off all the tape that was around him but as I did all his hairs where going off, he is now pink... all Pink and shivering, Poor harlie, I put him in a nice blanket, he walks around a blanket now, but stay on the sofa next to Grandma, she sometime give him some crisps too, mut his hair dont seem to grow back poor charlie, we love you Charlie.

This tea pot more thinking of Grandad as he likes bottoms a lot but would not admit it

Re-used hanger from sculpture by KS

181

THIS PAGE
WANTS A
BETTER
VIEW

THIS PAGE
DOES NOT LIKE
TO BE NEXT to
This OPPOSITE
PAGE

From: ███████████████████
To: <undisclosed-recipients:>
Sent: Monday, August 25, 2008 11:49 AM
Subject: meet me, you are the only...

Hi, I hope you are well.
I am so sorry for not giving you any news sooner.
Thank you for your concern and support, your thought were most kind. I hope you are well, I miss not seeing you passing by these days.

I am afraid to say that my Grandad conceptual plan to dig a tunnel below the city situation has not improved. Well, having no news from neither my Grandad and then my Grandma. I could not take the situation any more, so I decided that I had to go in the tunnel to find then.

On October the 1st I packed a good bag with enough food for a few days, a light, some match stick, a few bank notes and some cigarette. Just before leaving, I saw you by a bus stop in our area. I actually really liked what you where wearing, you looked very smart. Did you find the few yellow signs I had left for you?

I went to my grand parents garden, open the trap my Grandad had carefully hidden with leaves. The garden was in such a state completely overgrown.

I realised that my Grandad may have left with no money. My Grandma I couldn't care too much for her (she can be so irritating, arguing all the time), stressed, always shouting, pretending she cares. I would actually be quite happy if I was to never see her again. Before she left in the tunnel. She left me a note: 'My darling you are the most valuable thing I have. I am sorry to leave you like this but I feel that I have to go and find your Grandad. I am sure you remember us arguing a lot but you know how much I love him. I want to leave this with you in case anything happens (she left me her ring, trying to be super romantic... you see what kind of person she was?) Take care of yourself, I love you very much my darling x Grandma'

First when entering the tunnel I fell so badly, I did not expect it to be so stip, I got so muddy in the first few minutes, I must have been going down almost 60 meters, I recoaune. Then the tunnel was going in a straight line and was pretty flat, it was very dump down there and so dark. Some of the wooden structure my Grandad had put were starting to rot. In parts the ground was actually falling and blocking the way, luckily I saw a spade my gd must have left by mistake. I did use it quite often. After a few hours of walking I was taken by panic, what was I doing there? It was so depressing, I could hear some very strange sound, I was cold, full of mud.

185

I felt something gluey under my feet, a strange bid worm, I almost puked, the size of one arms. My light was not very strong, I would not see far. I found my self in front of a massive pipe, my Grandad must have come across it, not as planed, so the tunnel got dug down and around the pipe to find my self in same level on the other side, I had to climb in the mud, it was very slippery. I wish you could have been here with me but I would not have dared asking we hardly know each other.

On the other side of the pipe I got my light in direction of the tunnel and thought I could see some movement a person coming towards me. I got so scared, I wanted to scream, but as I walk closer it was only a piece of wood balancing from a string.

You know you are the only one I can tell what happened, nobody else knows (keep it for your self, I don't want the whole country to be on my case). After maybe 6 or 7 hours walking I started to wonder when it would end, I definitely had walked far more than across town, (no signs of life so far).

Then as the tunnel was getting slimmer I could see a crossing, the tunnel was taking two different direction. I sat down and try to position myself n the mind of my Grandad. Which direction should I take? I decided to go for the largest, what would you have done if you were me? I often thought about you and your advise when I was down there. The tunnel was very low not bigger than 1 metre diameter so it was nice to find my self in a bit bigger space. After 3 quater of an hour I could feel the tunnel to be slowly going up to the surface of the earth, I was so delighted. I could see the end coming, hear the sound of cars above me. I pushed a trap and here I was in the middle of some posh garden, and huge fields were surrounding a grand house. I looked around and hid my self in on of the bushes. I was out of town. I knew my Grandad had a very bad sense of orientation but I though after months of preparation he had plan better his piece. I try to get off some of the mud I had on my face with some leaves from the bush, I must have looked horrific. My Grandad must have been so disappointed to find himself there. After a few minutes, I could hear some people coming, I recognised a voice. My Grandma had her harm holding a posh old man (definitely not my Grandad), they were both talking like hahh a ha, she even put on a posh accent. They stopped by the bush, were laughing talking then she grabbed him and give him a big french kiss. I could not believe it. I jumped on them like whoa! they got so scared, ran towards the house. But my Grandma stopped and looked back, she walk back and recognised me I started to cry.

She has kept me in a warm bed for a few days now. I just asked her if I could contact you, so here it is for now. I need help as I have no idea where I am, my gd ma does not want to tell me, she says I am already under so much stress. But I need your help, tomorrow I will go back in the tunnel and try the other direction. I can't take it here being like a lemon... will let you know what is going on once I am on the other side.

See you soon I hope, I wish you all the best, Juan

----- Original Message -----
From: ███████████████████
To: <undisclosed-recipients:>
Sent: Wednesday, August 26 2008 01:14 AM
Subject: RE: meet me, you are the only...

Hello,
I hope you don't mind me contacting you, I got your e-mail through a friend.

I have seen you already quite a few time passing by our local video shop. I thought you seemed to be somebody very special, something about you intrigued me. You may have seen me before, I usually wear blue clothes and I have blue eyes. I leave a couple of roads away from you. I don't know if you remember that old man who used to walk around our neighbourgh hood by night. He actually was my Grandad. He was a famous artist who's work is owed by museums. He disappeared a few days ago.

He was half way to completion. He would start digging every morning from 6 am and was expected back by my Grandma by 8 pm to come home for dinner. But on Monday he did not come back. I have had no solution but contacting you to ask for your help, I do not want the press to get involved or make a public enquiry, nor have address revealed as the police should not hear of the matter as what he had done was highly illegal in this country. My Grandad has always been trying to push barriers and society rules as a very controversial artist. The last few days I saw him he looked highly suspicious. I hope nothing terrible happened to him in the tunnel. I don't wish to alarm any body.

But if you would have any idea or suggestions of what should I do would be more than welcome. If you can help me in any way, time, money, mental support. I choose to contact you as I did not wish to involve somebody too personal, as they would get alarmed and act un-accordingly,Thank you for your time, Best regards, and please excuse me if this e-mail sound a little strange,

Juan Roathlin

ps: You may see on your way home tomorrow a sign from me, something quite subtle, look care fully, one indication: it's yellow.

187

Hi Monika,
How goes it?? How is your mother? I've been thinking of you all week and then suddenly an email, ostensibly from you to me?? arrived-copy below. I noticed that the email was sent from you to yourself, does this make sense??
You may have a stalker, or did you this it was a "circular"-by the way, what are you doing on the 4th September??
Love,
Mary.

"Hello,
I don' t know if you remember but we meet some month ago very briefly at a party, you had to go pretty early...

Hope this email finds you well, be great to see you again, could you meet me on the 4th of September at Monika Bobinska Gallery, 242 Cambridge heath road, at 6pm i will be there waiting for you. Last week i saw you buying some shopping in your corner shop, but you seemed to be in a rush, i could not speak. You intimidate me.

I think you are someone quite special.

If you can not come on Thursday the 4th, I will be there every week Thursday to Sunday 1 to 6 till the 4th of October, I have a some interesting stories to tell you. My friend and i just came back from a big trip around the world, we have so much to show you and tell you about, some crazy things happened to us...

It would be nice to talk about your future plans, your new hair cut (which i acutely quite like), i will show you afilm i just made for you. My uncle might be there as well, he is just back from Egypt, where he was looking in the possibility of building a ski slop, i am sure you will find him fascinating.

He actually asked me to ask you if you may not be interested in financing it, it could be a very profitable business. I will be made by designer G J Grogy i know you are interested in the art this is project might be perfect for you.

Anyway we could talk about this in more detail when we meet. There is many things i would like to show you,share with you, You are the only one i really want to come, Meet me on the 4th of September 242 Cambridge heath road, at 6pm i will be there waiting for you.
I hope you can come, let me know,
Lind p"

----- Original Message -----
From: ▉▉▉▉▉▉▉▉▉▉▉▉▉▉▉▉▉▉▉▉
To: Monika Bobinska
Sent: Wednesday, August 27, 2008 12:36 PM
Subject: RE: meet me, you are the only...

Not for me I think.

----- Original Message -----
From: ▉▉▉▉▉▉▉▉▉▉▉▉▉▉▉▉▉▉▉▉
To: Monika Bobinska
Sent: Wednesday, August 27, 2008 12:48 PM
Subject: RE: meet me, you are the only...

Ski slopes in Egypt, eh...
Is Sept 4 a press view for the artist?
Best,
Chris

From: Monika Bobinska
Sent: 27 August 2008 14:36
To: ▉▉▉▉▉▉▉▉▉▉▉▉▉▉▉▉▉▉▉▉
Subject: Re: meet me, you are the only...

It might well be!!

----- Original Message -----
From: ▉▉▉▉▉▉▉▉▉▉▉▉▉▉▉▉▉▉
To: Monika Bobinska
Sent: Wednesday, August 27, 2008 4:53 PM

Subject: RE: meet me, you are the only...

And there was me thinking I had a secret admirer... is it just a case of turning up?

----- Original Message -----
From: ███████████████████████████
To: mail@monikabobinska.com
Sent: Wednesday, August 27, 2008 7:43 PM
Subject: Fw: meet me, you are the only...

Hi.
I get your regular updates for Lounge on line, but today I received this garbage
and thought you might like to be aware of it!
Regards,
Martin

----- Original Message -----
From: ████████████████████████
To: Monika Bobinska
Sent: Monday, September 08, 2008 6:20 PM
Subject: RE: meet me, you are the only...

Hi,
I am so sorry but only rcvd your message today, hence I missed you on the 4th.
I do hope you were not alone.
I have also been away on a big trip and had some very crazy things happen -
In fact these crazy things seem to follow me wherever I go.
It was so good to hear from you, thought you had forgotten me.
Sad you feel intimidated by me, perhaps if you knew me better you wouldn't feel
like that. I'd like to think so anyway.
Yes - I was in a rush at the corner shop that day - just getting a few things for
my trip. Shame I didn't see you
- Shame you felt unable to take the opportunity to speak to me.
And Yes again - I am a very special - BUT - I bet you are too.
Oh - Thanks, glad you liked the hair, cost a fortune.
I love Skiing and hope all is well with your uncle and his business plans.
Fortunately I may not be interested in financing his business but wish him all the
luck in the world - hope he makes his fortune.
My future plans - Wow! I have so many wonderful things I am going to do. One
of them is to be a famous artist, this will happen over the next five years so I am
sure we will meet again.

Thanks for thinking about me and I wish you all the best of everything.
Paula W

----- Original Message -----
From: ██████████████████
To: Monika Bobinska
Sent: Wednesday, August 27, 2008 10:36 PM
Subject: Re: meet me, you are the only...

is this a joke? i do not have a corner shop

----- Forwarded message from tequila911@cfl.rr.com -----
   Date: Wed, 27 Aug 2008 16:45:59 +0300
   From: Mike Oconnell <tequila911@cfl.rr.com>
Reply-To: Mike Oconnell <tequila911@cfl.rr.com>
 Subject: You got a message from "Lady272"

   * I am interested in Dating / Long-term Potential
   * Age: 27
   * Height: 5'6"
   * Body type: Average
   * Hair color: Blond
   * Ethnicity: White / Caucasian
   * Looks: Very attractive
   * Education: Graduate degree
   * Occupation: Other
   * Income: Not specified
   * I speak: English
   * Religion: Christian - other
   * Relationship status: Divorced
   * Children: No
   * Wants children: Undecided
   * Smoking: Never
   * Drinking: Rarely

Lady272.jpg
62K View Download

Message :
hi there,
i am interested in you,
get me back to my emailbox : lady4care@gmail.com

----- End forwarded message -----

----- Original Message -----
From: ███████████████████████
To: monika
Sent: Wednesday, August 27, 2008 1:48 PM
Subject: Re: meet me, you are the only...

What is this?

----- Original Message -----
From: ████████████████████████
To: Monika Bobinska
Sent: Wednesday, August 27, 2008 11:05 PM
Subject: Re: meet me, you are the only...

hey,
I don't remember meeting you. Which party did we meet at?
nice email.
Do you work at Monika Bobinska?
I may be able to come, will let you know.
T
ps did I give you my email address?

----- Original Message -----
From: ████████████████████████
Subject: meet me, you are the only...
To: "Monika Bobinska" <mail@monikabobinska.com>
Date: Wednesday, 27 August, 2008, 1:29 PM

"Hello,
I don' t know if you remember but we meet some month ago very briefly at a party,
you had to go pretty early...

Hope this email finds you well, be great to see you again, could you meet me on
the 4th of September at Monika Bobinska Gallery, 242 Cambridge heath road, at
6pm i will be there waiting for you. Last week i saw you buying some shopping

in your corner shop, but you seemed to be in a rush, i could not speak. You intimidate me.

I think you are someone quite special.

If you can not come on Thursday the 4th, I will be there every week Thursday to Sunday 1 to 6 till the 4th of October, I have a some interesting stories to tell you. My friend and i just came back from a big trip around the world, we have so much to show you and tell you about, some crazy things happened to us...

It would be nice to talk about your future plans, your new hair cut (which i acutely quite like), i will show you afilm i just made for you. My uncle might be there as well, he is just back from Egypt, where he was looking in the possibility of building a ski slop, i am sure you will find him fascinating.

He actually asked me to ask you if you may not be interested in financing it, it could be a very profitable business. I will be made by designer G J Grogy i know you are interested in the art this is project might be perfect for you.

Anyway we could talk about this in more detail when we meet. There is many things i would like to show you,share with you, You are the only one i really want to come, Meet me on the 4th of September 242 Cambridge heath road, at 6pm i will be there waiting for you.
I hope you can come, let me know,
Lind p"

----- Original Message -----
From: ███████████████████████████████
To: <undisclosed-recipients:>
Sent: Tuesday, September 02, 2008 1:38 AM
Subject: ***SPAM*** BARR: HIRZAN IZADY AND ASSOCIATES

I am Hirzan Izady from Malaysia, an attorney at law. A deceased client of mine died as the result of a heart-related condition on March 12th 2005.

His heart condition was due to the death of all the members of his family in the tsunami disaster on the 26th December 2004 in Sumatra Indonesia. http://en.wikipedia.org/wiki/2004_Indian_Ocean_earthquake.

My late Client has a deposit of Seventeen Million Five Hundred Thousand Dollars (US$17.5 Million Dollars) left behind. I have contacted you to assist in distributing the money left behind by my client before it is confiscated or declared unserviceable by the bank where this deposit valued at Seventeen million five hundrend dollars (US$17.5 million dollars) is lodged. This bank has issued me a notice to contact the next of kin, or the account will be confiscated.

My proposition to you is to seek your consent to present you as the next-of-kin and beneficiary of my named client so that the proceeds of this account can be paid to you.

Then we can share the amount on a mutually agreed-upon percentage. All legal documents to back up your claim as my client's next-of-kin will be provided. All I require is your honest cooperation to enable us see this transaction through.

This will be executed under a legitimate arrangement that will protect you from many breach of the law. If this business proposition offends your moral values, do accept my apology. I must use this opportunity to implore you to exercise the utmost indulgence to keep this matter extraordinary confidential, whatever your decision, while I await your prompt response.

Please contact me at once to indicate your interest. I will like you to acknowledge the receipt of this e-mail as soon as possible via my private EMAIL:(hirzanizady1@ hotmail.com) and treat with absolute confidentiality and sincerity. I look forward to your quick reply.

Best regards,
Barr Hirzan Izady
Attorney at Law

----- Original Message -----
From: ████████████████████████
To: Monika Bobinska
Sent: Tuesday, September 02, 2008 1:22 PM
Subject: Re: meet me, you are the only...

Monika, I have no iodea who is this person. Could you read the email below and shed some light on this man/ woman? Who is hse/ he? Howthis person emailed me? I do not wish to receive any emails from strangers. He/ She claims that she/ he met me. Where exactly and when as I feel that my privacy being threatened. I am ready to contact the police about the stalking, if I receive any more emails or you will give my email address to strangers.

How have you obtained my email in the first place?
Awaiting a prompt reply.
Jenny

----- Original Message -----
From: ▮▮▮▮▮▮▮▮▮▮▮▮▮▮▮▮▮▮
To: Monika Bobinska
Sent: Thursday, August 28, 2008 12:37 AM
Subject: RE: meet me, you are the only...

Hello,
Absoulutely, I know you and remeber you, and I am glad to hear from you.
But, I think you could be mistake me for the other. ^ ^ ;;;;
We met just through the group exhibiton about london to seoul seo gallery, not
a party. i am in london, just visiting, not a living.
So i will go back to seoul @ 3 Sep. If you would like to meet me, could you give
me more detail about the contents. Thanks,
Very regards

----- Original Message -----
From: ▮▮▮▮▮▮▮▮▮▮▮▮▮▮▮▮▮▮
To: Monika Bobinska
Sent: Thursday, August 28, 2008 3:21 PM
Subject: RE: meet me, you are the only...

Unfortunately this seems to have been sent to the wrong person.

----- Original Message -----
From: ▮▮▮▮▮▮▮▮▮▮▮▮▮▮▮▮▮▮
To: Monika Bobinska
Sent: Wednesday, August 27, 2008 1:08 PM
Subject: Re: meet me, you are the only...
Is this harassment?

----- Original Message -----
From: ▮▮▮▮▮▮▮▮▮▮▮▮▮▮▮▮▮▮
To: Monika
Sent: Wednesday, August 27, 2008 1:12 PM
Subject: Re: meet me, you are the only...

hi monika
just saw this email from you - did you forward it to me by mistake - it looks very
strange, hope all is well otherwise

~ Lesley

From: ██████████████████████
To: <undisclosed-recipients:>
Sent: Thursday, September 04, 2008 5:19 AM
Subject: ***SPAM*** Greetings My Dear

Greetings My Dear

I am writting this letter with due respect and heartful of tears since we have not known or met ourselves previously.

I am asking for your assistance after I have gone through a profile that speaks good of you. I will be so glad if you can allow and lead me to the right channel towards your assistance to our situation now. I will make my proposal well known if I am given the opportunity. I would like to use this opportunity to introduce myself to you. well, I am Peter Williams 22 and my younger sister Sandra Williams is 19. I know that this proposal might be a surprise to you but do consider it as an emmergency.

In nutshell, our late father Cheif Andrew Williams ,was the personal advicer to the former head of state in my country Sierra Leone in west Africa But he was killed along side with my mother during the longing civil war and all his properties was totally destroyed. However, after their death we managed to escape with a very important document (deposit certificate) of u.s ($ 6,000,000.00) Six Million U.S dollars deposited by our late father in a Bank which we are the next of kins.

Meanwhile,I am saddled with the problem of securing a trust worthy foriegn personality to help us transfer the money over to his country and into his possession pending our arrival to meet with him.

Furthermore, you can contact the Bank here in Cote D'Ivoire for confirmation and i will issue a letter of Introduction as our Guildian/Trustee, that will enable the Bank to deal with you on our behalf. We are giving you this offers as mentioned with every confidence on your acceptance to assist us or take us as your children and manage the money.I will also be happy if you can come over here in Cote D'Ivoire to see us and at the same time handle the transfer process.

Conclusively, i wish you send us a reply immediately as soon as you recieve this proposal. for confidential purposes, your urgent reply will be highly appreciated. You can call us on our mobile number:+22547476705

Thank you for your corporation
Yours faithfully
Peter and Sandra Williams.

----- Original Message -----
From: ████████████████████████████████
To: < mail@monikabobinska.com>
Sent: Wednesday, August 27, 2008 1:47 PM
Subject: RE: meet me, you are the only...

Hi Monika
I got this from you and am not sure who it is from as I do not remember such
a person.
Are you sure it is for me? I'm finding it quite surreal!
If you sent it to me erroneously, could you just let me know - and if not, could
you give me any clues as to who Lind P is?
I don't want to enter into correspondence with her without any of this knowledge!
Cheers and hope you're well. I'm in Newfoundland, back soon, see you then.
Paulx

----- Original Message -----
From: ████████████████████████████████
To: Monika Bobinska
Sent: Wednesday, August 27, 2008 2:45 PM
Subject: Re: meet me, you are the only...

Very odd mail?

----- Original Message -----
From: ███████████████████
To: Monika Bobinska
Sent: Wednesday, August 27, 2008 6:57 PM
Subject: Re: meet me, you are the only...

What is this? My fiancee read it and I had some explaining to do.

----- Original Message -----
From: ████████████
To: Monika Bobinska
Sent: Thursday, August 28, 2008 10:58 AM
Subject: RE: meet me, you are the only...

hi Monika,
back in action now.
This is wierd! Can't remember her. Can you? Sponsoring a ski slope? I wish
Like the bit about the hair cut
speak soon
John

----- Original Message -----
From: █████████████████████
To: Monika Bobinska
Sent: Sunday, August 31, 2008 2:04 PM
Subject: RE: meet me, you are the only...

Ok,
I confess I don't remember you-where did we meet, what party, how did you
get my e-mail address??? It all sounds very interesting but I'm gonna need
my memory jogged a bit first. If this is an art project or a hook to get people
through the doors of Monika Bobinska then hats off for inventivness-if this is
for real then please fill in some gaps... I thought I had a pretty good memory.
All the best...
ps.the fact that I read your mail JUST after having had my hair cut was a little
strange...

----- Original Message -----
From: █████████████████
To: < mail@monikabobinska.com >

Sent: Friday, August 29, 2008 6:55 PM
Subject: RE: meet me, you are the only...

Dear Monika,
I received this e-mail from your account. I don't know if it is with reference to a art project that is happening. I found the e-mail a little disconcerting particularly references to the corner shop and the hair cut, the film made of me, and meeting an unknown person, since I have been harassed in the past.
This eventually involved the police who cautioned the man in question under the Harassment Act. If the police had found the evidence on his digital camera or his laptop then he would have been prosecuted and got a 2 year suspended sentence.
Please put my mind at rest over this e-mail. Otherwise I will need to take the matter further, this will involve checking with my service provider if my account has been hacked into, talking to the Internet Cafe about their security systems, and then taking a copy of the e-mail to the police station.
Best Wishes
Mark

----- Original Message -----
From: ███████████████████████
To: Monika Bobinska
Sent: Sunday, August 31, 2008 9:42 AM
Subject: RE: meet me, you are the only...

Linda,
I sent a reply to your googlemail address. Could you reply to that or this.
Wed is poss but please simplify...
Alec

199

THIS PAGE
THINKS YOU
LOOK GREAT
FROM HERE

this page
provoke LIGHTNING
AS YOU READ

3

regime of modern personal

critical art — march

some work
avant garde and the culture
for people

women strange — re in...
manhattan society
re int reduce
to be used — made man

eng

woo... pouring pen
drank not making
sense

as if he has Been leave
in a Burren away

society

clearly in
darkness

about under

different
angle
tell...

on person

the camera Ben
the narrator surrounding

Shooting indoors:

- Eye looking
- One finger moving
- Shakespeare
- Life or death / existentialism
- Man-woman differences - different body
- Food- canard en sauce...
- Going up stairs - slow motion
- Skin touching - neck move
- Ears
- Music - visual equivalence
- Stop - twenty minute watch speak-up
- Hairy plant / studio- so hairy
- Took off clothes
- Dirty / naked no time to put clothes
- Drips from cloves
- Pulling something
- Relax - sleeping
- Hand on paper doing drawing
- Smashing paper in one hand
- Scratches on paper-visual noise for sound
- Going through door - slam
- Gelatine / honey slimy room
- Lock-padlock closing
- Heat - sweat on someone - hardly breath
- Crack
- Water leak
- Thinks coming out of holes
- Legs up
- Socks coming out of weird holes
- Paint dripping
- ...eat
- ...e melting on skin
- ...ing up and down
- ...alloon
- Steam- bath
- Running down stairs
- Door slamming
- Naked feet through door/dirty
- TV entertainment
- Comfortable living room
- Something stuck behind doors
- Hand on naked bottom pushing
- Blood- scrashes
- Metal on tooth/ice cube
- George Michael looking
- Rope tight hard around hand
- Piece of burning wood or matches 10 at once
- Beating smash towards one face
- Caresses
- Smile (she was please to see me)
- Holding tight
- Hand on shoulder

Shooting outdoors:

- Go north (finger in wind) feet in the floor showing direction
- Slide
- Better digging
- Running
- Something falling down (slide)
- Stuck / between wood/wire

Handwritten annotations include: STUDIO, MAN, BOY, shaking something - pear, EXIST - EN - TIRLISM, Exit sign, out doors, studio, me, George Michael, strange people, hands in front, smile clean, plastic Bag in front of mouth, painting wash, MAN - WOMAN differ, exit sign, strawberry being scashed / Boiled, man feet, man woman

Text: PLAY

Dialogue: Well I'm back it wasn't very important
            Thank you for coming

Text: THANK YOU FOR COMING

Dialogue: I'm going to point things out. I thought you might need to
            see my hand there, just a little bit. Like, I'm talking to
            you there, there. I hope your sat quite well in your chair.

Text: I AM SORRY THIS ROOM IS NOT SO NICE, I DID ASK FOR IT TO BE
            CHANGED WITH BEAUTIFUL FURNITURES, PAINTINGS AND SOFAS. BUT
            THEY DID NOT LISTEN I HOPE YOU ARE NOT TOO COLD

Dialogue: So I wish the screen was a little bit bigger

Text: OR AT LEAST A LARGER IMAGE

Dialogue: So we could have a bit more, it would be nice if you could
            see my head and my legs. You'll have to imagine my face now,
            like its projected above you there. You know it would be on
            the ceiling, there, floating above you. You know it might be
            a bit distorted now, with the pipe and everything. You'll have
            to imagine my arms are on the wall. As if I'm talking and
            embracing the room.

Text: SORRY

Dialogue: I wish we got the image a bit smaller or the room, or the
            screen a bit bigger you know

Text: IF WE HAD NICE SOFAS WE COULD HAVE SOME MUSIC PLAYING AND
            TALK ABOUT LOVE, SCIENCE, PHILOSOPHY...

Dialogue: Last week my mother and me were talking about time. Well,
            time is not time, time is speed. So like your not seeing me
            as I am now

Text: Spacetime is usually interpreted with space being three-
            dimensional and time playing the role of the fourth dimension

Dialogue: and then again I am a projection of what I am now

Text: quantum mechanics and general relativity into a quantum
            theory of gravity.

Dialogue: and the person next to you is just you missing him a few
            second, a quarter, a quarter of seconds

Text: Time is a relation in space. Thus, an hour and time it
            defines, produced and regulated by cosmic dynamism,

Dialogue: because it's speed on light on you

Text: appears to be of a very different reality than space: more
            mysterious and more exalted, intangible and immutable.

Dialogue: well it's never, it's not the real you or the real moment, or the real person

Text: Time, understood as a scale of variables as the fourth of a system of coordinates

Dialogue: Maybe its wrong but

Text: BUT THATS WHAT MY MOTHER TOLD ME

Dialogue: I've heard it, it's all about speed I've heard

Text: Nevrtheless, just as all things which preoccupy man, the fourth dimension-like the unicorn, acquiring evidence.

Dialogue: it's what my mother told me, it's about speed. You might be here for quite some time you know. Because I don't know how long this video is going to be

Text: as a four dimensional continuum in which all material accidents are situated by four spatio-temporal variables;

Dialogue: See because the thing is because I'm here on screen on video,

Text: THIS FOOD LOOKS SO GOOD

Dialogue: I'll never age. Speed and time I don't really care,

Text: just as it had substituted itself for primitive flat schematizations of the earth and heavens;

Dialogue: but you are you, you are ageing, even here

Text: if the indivisible unity of the four factors of space-time is slowly acquiring evidence.

Dialogue: watching this you are slowly

Text: OLD

Dialogue: getting old

Text: OLD

Dialogue: I'm happy we are here together. I'm sure there is noise in your space here as well

Text: DID YOU SEE WHO IS IN THE ROOM WITH YOU
            HERE SOME MORE LIGHT SO YOU CAN SEE BETTER THE ROOM AND WHO IS THERE

Dialogue: Or you try to be quiet because there is this projection going. But you can talk you know, I don't mind. You can talk over me I'm just

Text: I WILL TURN DOWN THE SOUND

Dialogue: just trying to

Text: AND SLOWLY DESEAPER

Dialogue: When I was walking around the building this morning, I saw
             that

Text: BY THE STAIRS

Dialogue: and it jumped on my face, I think it's still on my back. I
             think its crawling down. it must be in the room now, in your
             room.

Text: DON'T LOOK UP

Dialogue: I couldn't see, but I think I can see it on the left wall
             there. Its great you could come you know, I'm really happy.
             But sometimes don't really mind if your here or not, you know,
             if your not here I'll just keep carry on talking, I'll just go
             on and I quite enjoy my company really so

Text: WITH MY AUNTIES AND THEIR DOG WE WENT LOOKING AT DIFFERENT
             FABRICS TO IMPROVE THE SITS

Dialogue: I'll just be here talking like nothing happened. Its quite a
             big room where we are. I like your hair of course. If you need
             to have a cigarette, I don't mind you can help yourself, you
             can have a cigarette, if you get into trouble, just tell them
             I say its okay. Its not just about me here, you know its about
             us all in the room.

Text: MAYBE YOU WOULD PREFER TO BE THERE WITH FRIENDS NOT HERE IN
             THIS ROOM
             UNFORTUNATLY WE ARE IN THIS ROOM AND NOT WITH THOSE PEOPLE

Dialogue: Imagine the person next to you is naked, completely naked.

Text: YOU ARE EMBARRASSED AND TURNING RED

Dialogue: Don't look now, just imagine. You know the doors are closed
             and they're not going to know.

Text: HAVE A CIGARETTE
             EDITING

Dialogue: If your a bit hot you can take off your shirt.

Text: I CAN IMAGINE YOU ALL IN SWIMMING COSTUME

Dialogue: I really don't mind.

Text: I THINK YOU LOOK QUITE GOOD FROM HERE

Dialogue: I really don't mind again. We're absolutely fine.

Text: SKIPPING PROJECTOR
             CONCENTRATE

YESTERDAY HERE A VERY FAT MAN WITH A RED MOUSTACHE STTOD UP
IN FRONT OF THE SCREEN

Dialogue: He was going away on, like he would go in front of the screen

Text: IT WAS VERY ENOYING
             MY JUMPER WAS GOING ALL DISTORTED

Dialogue: he was so badly behaved. Not like you today. Your very nice
             you know. They were just craziness. I know look, look. I just
             saw a mouse. It was just beneath where the screen is there.
             Just there. And then an old lady got really pissed off. Like
             screaming, like, she was like, she put ketchup everywhere,
             like we were all insistent as well, like we were covered in
             ketchup. And then she put some all over the screen as well.
             All over me. I had some like all over my jumper there. I
             couldn't get rid of it. You can see there's still a bit of
             red on the side of the wall, if you look carefully.

Text: THE OLD LADY TOOK THE OLD MAN MOUSTACHE

Dialogue: Then she started putting the moustache like so strongly,
             the big red moustache off this man

Text: I WAS WORRIED WHAT THEY WERE GOING TO DO TO ME

Dialogue: It was so strongly and some blood was coming and everywhere

Text: SO I JUST LEFT QUIETLY THE SCREEN
             THEY DID NOT REALISE I WAS GONE

Dialogue: Its was happened the other day, you know I'm not making
             things up. I not making things up.

Text: WHEN YOU LEAVE

Dialogue: You can ask the girl at the entrance there. She was there.
             But we don't really want to talk about it. We don't want bad
             publicity or anything. Cut. Look what I've done. I got all
             the clothes from the heating. I collected them from everywhere
             and I put them all there. Exactly where I was making the
             video. And I folded them like, and for you it was not time
             but for me, it was like twenty minutes. So you see I've been
             quite productive. Being in the room here watching this film.
             Your not exactly doing that much at least you know, I'm making
             a video. And I'm folding the clothes. You know when you leave
             the room well I'm still doing something. Oh I'm sorry, can
             the person with the dog leave the room.

Text: THIS NICE DOG IS WAITING OUTSIDE TOO

Dialogue: now please because I really can't concentrate, you know I
             can't, I can't talk, making a film and a dog is barking at
             the same time I can't do it, it's too much for me. Oh, I
             knew it would be someone at the door, I'm going to get it.

Text: IT SO NICE OUTSIDE

- Hardly breath - plastic bag in front of mouth
- Many children
- Slide
- Better digging
- Running
- Something falling down (slide)
- Stuck / between wood/wire
- People looking at what s happening/bus stop wait
- Police
- Gallop
- Shooting in leg, throwing stones
- Traffic light turning green
- More leg on concrete
- Skin dragged on pavement
- Night shooting of action people talking
- Bell button
- Looking through window for pig
- Cry someone crying
- Machine crushing things
- Children playing
- People in bus
- Water hose
- Kiss on mouth
- Milky way
- Hand on car wheel
- Tire turning brutal
- Man shoes on brake
- Lines on alfast-concrete
- Balloon
- Shooting everywhere
- Concert poster/instrument
- Pulling something
- Man-woman differences- different body
- Teaching / Belgium guy
- Girlfriend / hand in hand
- Gang of people
- Old woman face / asking question
- Many bottle of milk
- Really dirty - birds cleaning

CHAPTER 4

FILM

This is a Film

THIS MORNING
I WOKE UP
MOVED THE
SHEETS TO MY
LEFT WITH MY
RIGHT HAND...

It was s

entle...

NEXT TO ME
WAS THIS MAN

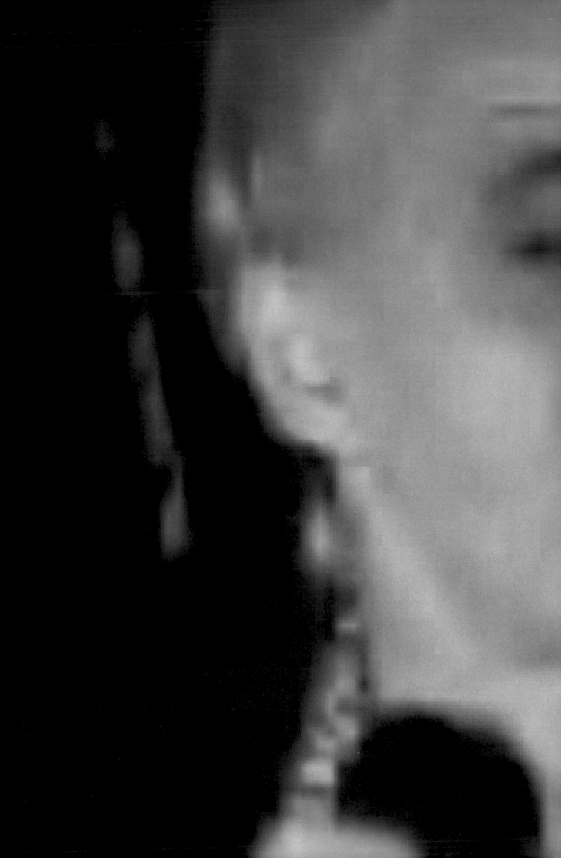

SEEING
YOU THERE
LOOKING
THE GUY DID
HOLD YOUR
ARM FIRMLY
AND TOOK
YOU TO WHAT
FOLLOWS

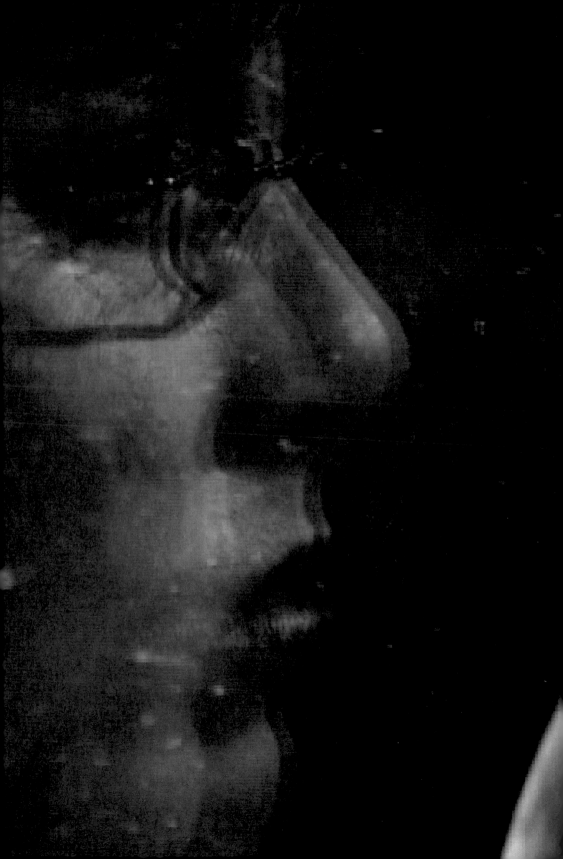

HE THREW YOU
IN A BUS NEXT
TO THAT LADY

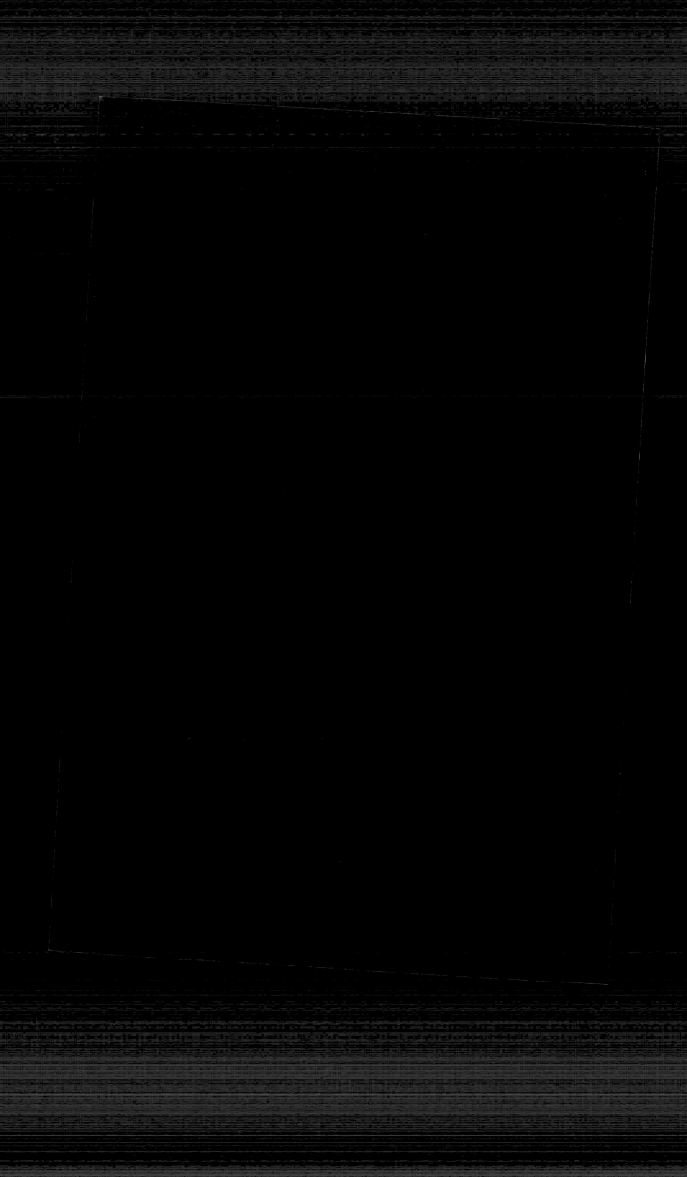

ON THE OTHER SIDE OF THE WORLD A WOMAN WAS REPORTING THE EVENT

NCN your heart

IN ANGER HE
BROKE THE
BUS WINDOW

IT DID HURT
LIKE THIS
BUT THE GLAS
WAS SHARP
NOT JUST
AN IMAGE

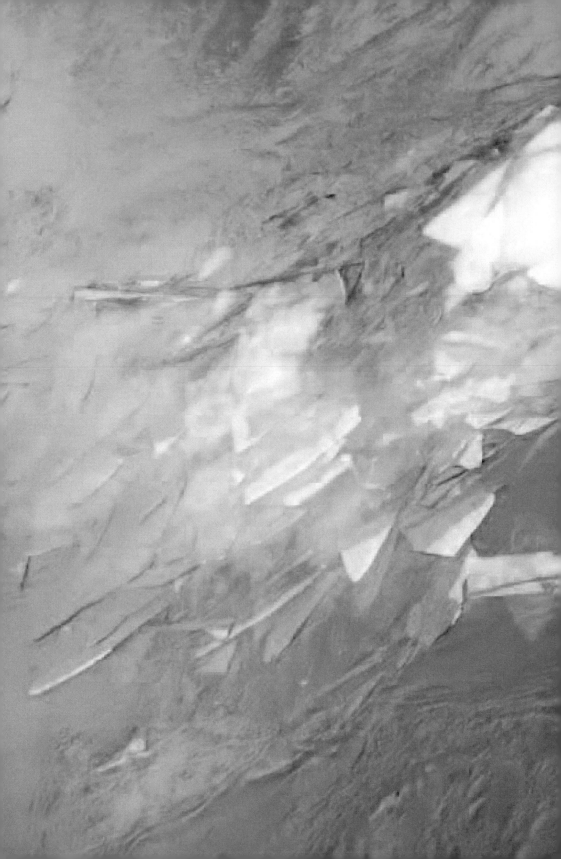

THE PAPER WAS CUTTING LIKE A THIN KNIFE ON YOUR SKIN

And galopped every where

nd we arrived by the sea...

YOU SAW
A BOAT AND
A MAN BEING
PULLED INTO
THE WATER
BY A PIG

And, And, And i went to

e every body and said,

BLINDED THEY
DIVED DEEP
DOWN THE
PAPER

They drove me to a sort of camp,

ere we were carrying bags of stuff.

YOU TRIED TO
HIDE BEHIND
THE PAGES

THE POLICE
IS LOOKING
FOR THEM
THEY THINK
THEY ARE
WITH YOU

THERE WAS

THROUING G

IMAGINE GETT

OF GREEN,

DRIBBLIN

A MACHINE

REEN AT ME.

NG COVERED

UFOCATING.

GREEN.

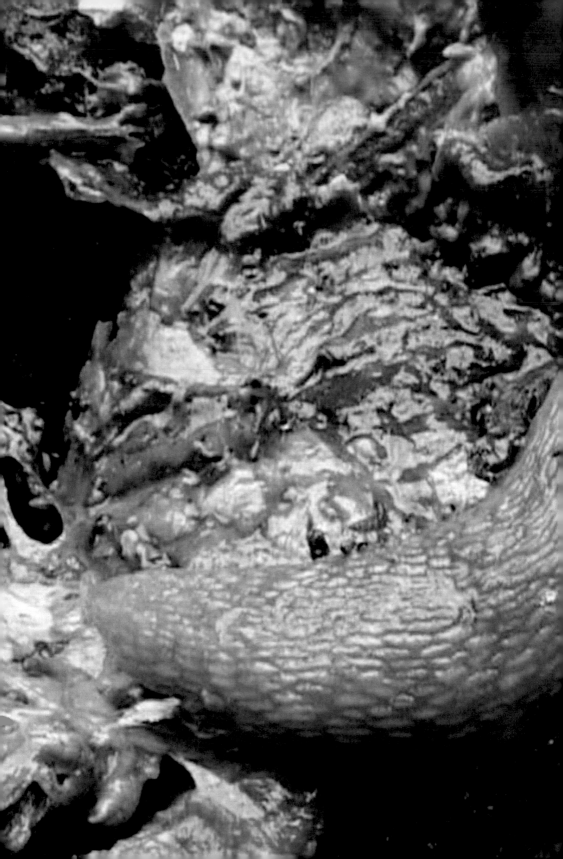

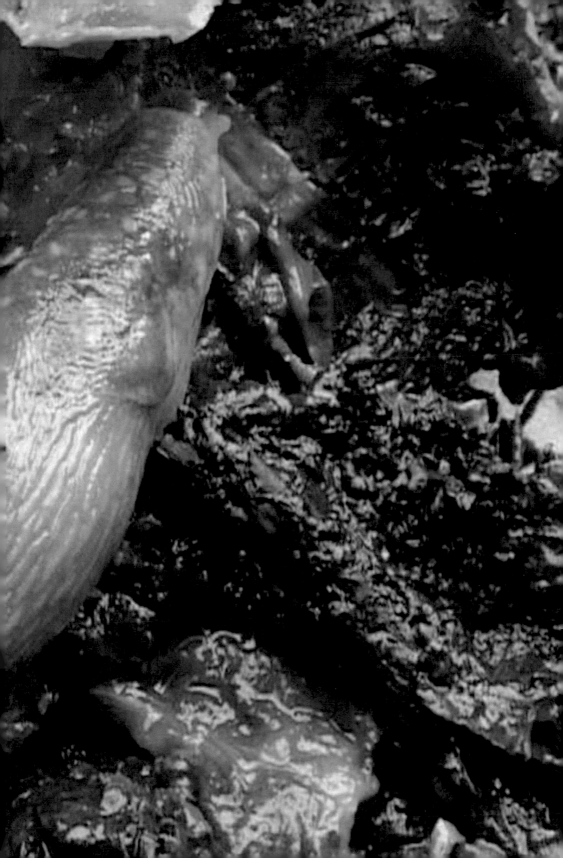

YOU SLIPPED
IT WAS SO
SLIMEY

IF I WAS YOU I WOULD BE SCARED TO TURN THE PAGE

HE DROPPED
HIS DRUM TO
HELP YOU HIDE

HE DID NOT
WANT TO BE ON
THE PREVIOUS
PAGE BUT
TO BE LYING
NAKED IN
YOUR PALM

IT BURNS YOUR HAND, IT, IT, HEAT, HIT

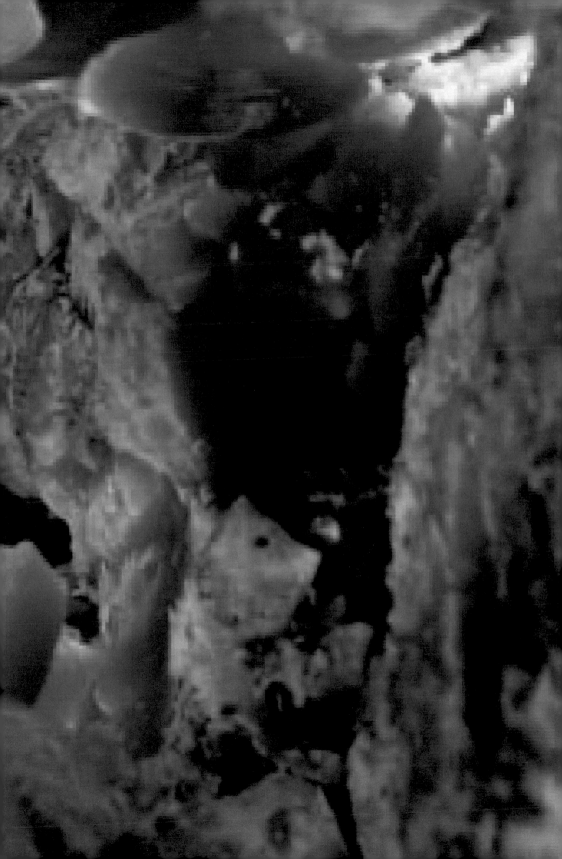

ALL THE INK
OF THIS BOOK
WAS DRIPPING

THE CAT WILL LICK IT

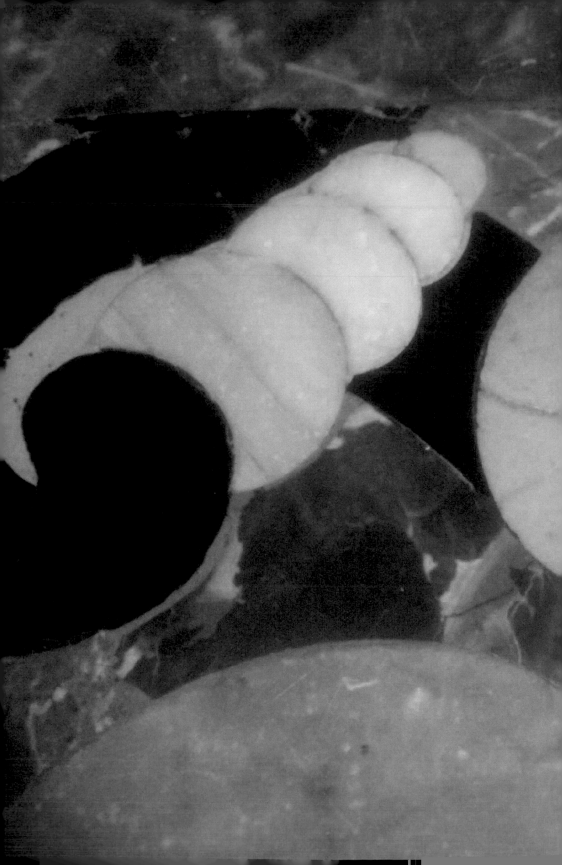

YOU JUMP

YOU ARE
DROWNING AND
SWALLOWING
THIS TEXT

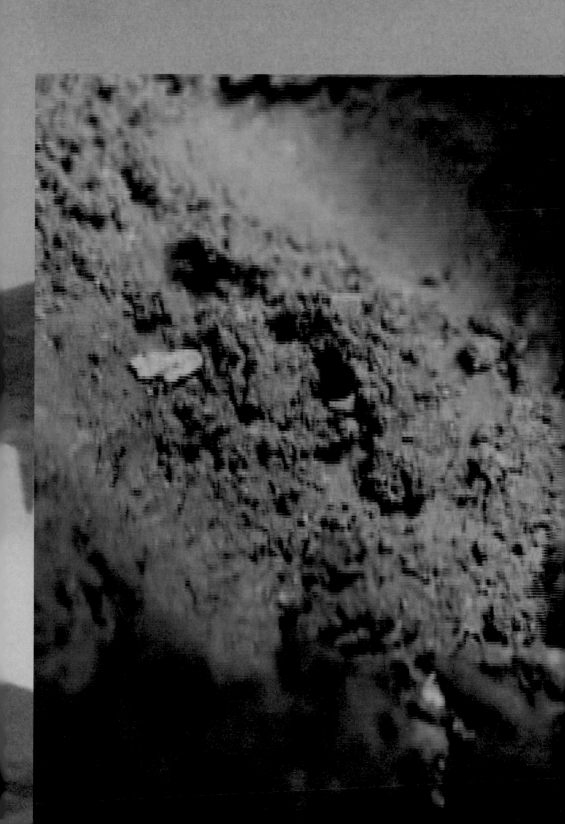

THEN
EVERYTHING
TURNED

GEORGE
MICHAEL
WAS THERE
LOOKING
NOT DOING
ANYTHING

50 HORSES GALLOPING TOWARD YOUR EYES FROM HERE

BRINGING WITH THEM A BLAST OF FRESH WIND IN YOUR FACE

Acknowledgements

Biography contributions in order of appearance, 'Early Years' by
Melissa Gronlund, 'Adolescence' by Nick Aikens, 'The Artist's
Drive' by Will Holder, 'The Artist and Drugs' by Emily Wardill,
'Being Misunderstood' by Simon Bedwell, 'The Artist's Only Love'
by Cally Spooner, 'The Artist's Special Show' by Stewart Home,
'Travels' by Rory Macbeth, 'The Artist's Contemporaries' by Isla
Leaver-Yap, 'The Forgotten Artist' by Mike Sperlinger, 'Depression'
by Katrina Palmer and 'The Artist's Secret' by Lynda Morris

'Early Works and Influences' contains found drawings and
paintings, including works by Tom Humphreys and Alex Cecchetti

'Eight Responses' originally published in *8 Metaphors (because the
moving image is not a book)*, ed. Isla Leaver-Yap, published by
LUX, London, 2011

'Group Show August' courtesy Francesco Pedraglio, originally
published in *Mousse* issue 26, November 2010

Spam emails in 'Personal Communications' courtesy
Laure Prouvost and Monika Bobinska Gallery, London

Cover images by Laure Prouvost, from *Altered Book*, 2013,
after Georges Bataille, *L'Abbé C*, Modern Classics, Penguin,
London, 2012

Thanks to MOT International, London

The Artist Book
Laure Prouvost

Published and distributed by Book Works
Designed by Fraser Muggeridge studio
Edited by Gavin Everall, Jane Rolo, Camilla Wills
Printed by Cassochrome, Belgium

ISBN 978 1 906012 44 1

Book Works is funded by Arts Council England. This publication
is generously supported by The Henry Moore Foundation.

Book Works, 19 Holywell Row, London, EC2A 4JB
www.bookworks.org.uk
+44 (0)207 247 2203